OLD MOORE

HOROSCOPE AND ASTRAL DIARY

TAURUS

OLD MOORE'S

HOROSCOPE AND ASTRAL DIARY

TAURUS

foulsham
LONDON • NEW YORK • TORONTO • SYDNEY

W. Foulsham & Co. Ltd

for Foulsham Publishing Ltd
The Old Barrel Store, Drayman's Lane, Marlow, Bucks SL7 2FF

Foulsham books can be found in all good bookshops and direct from
www.foulsham.com

ISBN: 978-0-572-04690-3

Copyright © 2017 Foulsham Publishing Ltd

A CIP record for this book is available from the British Library

Printed in Great Britain by Martins The Printers, Berwick-upon-Tweed

CONTENTS

INTRODUCTION

Astrology has been a part of life for centuries now, and no matter how technological our lives become, it seems that it never diminishes in popularity. For thousands of years people have been gazing up at the star-clad heavens and seeing their own activities and proclivities reflected in the movement of those little points of light. Across centuries countless hours have been spent studying the way our natures, activities and decisions seem to be paralleled by their predictable movements. Old Moore, a time-served veteran in astrological research, continues to monitor the zodiac and has produced the Astral Diary for 2018, tailor-made to your own astrological makeup.

Old Moore's Astral Diary is unique in its ability to get the heart of your nature and to offer you the sort of advice that might come from a trusted friend. It enables you to see in a day-by-day sense exactly how the planets are working for you. The diary section advises how you can get the best from upcoming situations and allows you to plan ahead successfully. There's also room on each daily entry to record your own observations or appointments.

While other popular astrology books merely deal with your astrological 'Sun sign', the Astral Diaries go much further. Every person on the planet is unique and Old Moore allows you to access your individuality in a number of ways. The front section gives you the chance to work out the placement of the Moon at the time of your birth and to see how its position has set an important seal on your overall nature. Perhaps most important of all, you can use the Astral Diary to discover your Rising Sign. This is the zodiac sign that was appearing over the Eastern horizon at the time of your birth and is just as important to you as an individual as is your Sun sign.

It is the synthesis of many different astrological possibilities that makes you what you are and with the Astral Diaries you can learn so much. How do you react to love and romance? Through the unique Venus tables and the readings that follow them, you can learn where the planet Venus was at the time of your birth. It is even possible to register when little Mercury is 'retrograde', which means that it appears to be moving backwards in space when viewed from the Earth. Mercury rules communication, so be prepared to deal with a few setbacks in this area when you see the sign ☿. The Astral Diary will be an interest and a support throughout the whole year ahead.

Old Moore extends his customary greeting to all people of the Earth and offers his age-old wishes for a happy and prosperous period ahead.

THE ESSENCE OF TAURUS

Exploring the Personality of
Taurus the Bull

(21ST APRIL – 21ST MAY)

What's in a sign?

Taurus is probably one of the most misunderstood signs of the zodiac. Astrologers from the past described those born under the sign of the Bull as being gentle, artistic, stubborn and refined. All of this is quite true, but there is so much more to Taureans and the only reason it isn't always discussed as much as it should be is because of basic Taurean reserve. Taureans are generally modest, and don't tend to assert themselves in a direct sense, unless in self-defence. As a result the sign is often sidelined, if not ignored.

You know what you want from life and are quite willing to work long and hard to get it. However, Taurus is also a great lover of luxury, so when circumstances permit you can be slow, ponderous and even lax. If there is a paradox here it is merely typical of Venus-ruled Taurus. On differing occasions you can be chatty or quiet, bold or timorous, smart or scruffy. It all depends on your commitment to a situation. When you are inspired there is nobody powerful enough to hold you back and when you are passionate you have the proclivities of a Casanova!

There are aspects of your nature that seldom change. For example, you are almost always friendly and approachable, and invariably have a sense of what feels and looks just right. You are capable and can work with your hands as well as your brain. You don't particularly care for dirt or squalid surroundings, preferring cleanliness, and you certainly don't take kindly to abject poverty. Most Taureans prefer the country to the coast, find loving relationships easy to deal with and are quite committed to home and family.

Whilst variety is the spice of life to many zodiac signs this is not necessarily the case for Taurus. Many people born under the sign of the Bull remain happy to occupy a specific position for years on end. It has been suggested, with more than a grain of truth, that the only thing that can get the Bull moving on occasions is a strategically placed bomb. What matters most, and which shows regularly in your dealings with the world at large, is your innate kindness and your desire to help others.

Taurus resources

The best word to describe Taurean subjects who are working to the best of their ability would be 'practical'. Nebulous situations, where you have to spend long hours thinking things through in a subconscious manner, don't suit you half as much as practical tasks, no matter how complex these might be. If you were to find yourself cast up on a desert island you would have all the necessities of life sorted out in a flash. This is not to suggest that you always recognise this potential in yourself. The problem here is that a very definite lack of self-belief is inclined to make you think that almost anyone else in the world has the edge when it comes to talent. Another of your greatest resources is your creative potential. You always have the knack of knowing what looks and feels just right. This is as true when it comes to decorating your home as it is regarding matters out there in the big, wide world. If this skill could be allied to confidence on a regular basis, there would be little or nothing to stop you. You may well possess specific skills which others definitely don't have, and you get on best when these are really needed.

Taureans don't mind dealing with routine matters and you have a good administrative ability in a number of different fields. With a deeply intuitive streak (when you are willing to recognise it), it isn't usually hard for you to work out how any particular individual would react under given circumstances. Where you fall down on occasions is that you don't always recognise the great advantages that are yours for the taking, and self-belief could hardly be considered the Taurean's greatest virtue.

Taurus people are good at making lists, even if these are of the mental variety. Your natural warmth makes it possible for you to find friends where others would not, and the sort of advice that you offer is considered and sensible. People feel they can rely on you, a fact that could prove to be one of the most important of your resources. There is nothing at all wrong with using this ability to feather your own nest, particularly since you are not the sort of person who would willingly stand on those around you in order to get where you want to go.

Beneath the surface

To say that you are deep would be a definite understatement. Only you know how far down into the basement some of your considerations and emotions actually go. Because you exhibit a generally practical face to the world at large the true scope of the Taurean mind remains something of a mystery to those around you. Certainly you seem to be uncomplicated and even a little superficial at times, though nothing could be further from the truth. Very little happens to you that fails to be filed away in some recess or other of that great interior that is your mind's library. It may be because of this that Taurus is well known for being able to bear a grudge for a long time. However, what is sometimes forgotten is that you never let a kindness from someone else go without reward, even though it may take you a very long time to find a way to say thank you.

Affairs of the heart are of special importance to you and ties of the romantic kind go as deep as any emotion. Once you love you tend to do so quite unconditionally. It takes months or years of upsets to shake your faith in love, and it's a fact that even in these days of marital splits, Taureans are far more likely than most signs of the zodiac to remain hitched. The simple fact is that you believe in loyalty, absolutely and irrevocably. The thought of letting anyone down once you have given your word is almost unthinkable and if such a situation does occur there are almost always quite definite mitigating factors.

Rules and regulations are easy for you to deal with because you have a natural tendency to order. You are also fairly good at dealing with routines and probably have your own life well sorted out as a result. A word of caution is necessary only when this internal need for order extends too much into your external life. Taureans can be fanatical about having a tidy house or for making things work out exactly as they would wish in a work sense. These tendencies start within the recesses of your own, often closed, mind. The way forward here is to throw open the doors and windows now and again and to let those around you know how you function internally. It isn't easy, because you are quite a closed book at heart. However the exercise is well worthwhile and the results can be quite breathtaking.

Making the best of yourself

Anyone who wants to work to the best of their ability first needs a good deal of self-knowledge. In your case this means recognising just what you are capable of doing and then concentrating in these directions. Of course it's only human nature to want to be all the things we are not, but this tendency runs deeper in you than it does in the majority of individuals. Use your natural kindness to the full and ally this to your practical ability to get things done. Sorting things out is easy for you, so easy in fact that you sometimes fail to realise that not everyone has these skills to the same extent.

Confidence definitely seems to be evident in the way you deal with the world at large. Of course you know that this often isn't the case, but that doesn't matter. It's the way the world at large views you that counts, so keep moving forward, even on those occasions when you are shaking inside. Use your naturally creative skills to the full and cultivate that innate sense of order in ways that benefit you and the world at a very practical level.

Avoid the tendency to be stubborn by convincing yourself that so many things 'simply don't matter'. An inability to move, simply because you feel annoyed or aggrieved, is certainly going to be more of a hindrance than a help – though there are occasions when, like all facets of nature, it's essential. Cultivate the more cheerful qualities that are endemic to your nature and be prepared to mix freely with as many different sorts of people as you possibly can. Be willing to take on new responsibilities because the more you are able to do so, the greater is your natural sense of self-worth. Stitching all these qualities together and using them to your own advantage isn't always easy, but pays handsomely in the end.

The impressions you give

This is a very interesting section as far as the sign of Taurus is concerned. The reason is very simply that you fail on so many occasions to betray the sheer depth of your own Earth-sign nature. That doesn't mean to say that you come across badly to others. On the contrary, you are probably a very popular person, except with those people who mistreat or cheat others. You have a great sense of what is right, and don't tend to deviate from a point of view once you've come to terms with it.

The world sees you as capable, cheerful and generally active, though with a tendency to be sluggish and lethargic on occasions. Perhaps Taurus needs to explain itself more because even when you are not at your most vibrant best there are invariably reasons. You can be quite secretive, though only usually about yourself. This can make life with the Taurean something of a guessing game on occasions. Certainly you appear to be much more fixed in your attitude than might often be the case. Why should this be so? It's mainly because you do have extremely definite ideas about specific matters, and since you sometimes display these it's natural that others pigeon-hole you as a very 'definite' sort. Actually this is far from being the whole truth but, once again, if you don't explain yourself, others can be left in the dark.

You almost certainly are not short of friends. People recognise that you are friendly, tolerant and extremely supportive. You give the impression of being very trustworthy and people know that they can rely on you to act in a specific manner. If this appears to make you somewhat predictable it doesn't really matter because you are deeply loved, and that's what counts. One fact is almost certain – the world has a greater regard for you in a general sense than you have for yourself.

The way forward

The ideal life for the Taurus subject seems to be one that is settled and happy, with not too much upheaval and plenty of order. Whether or not this truly turns out to be the case depends on a number of factors. For starters, even those born under the sign of the Bull have a boredom threshold. This means that having to respond to change and diversity probably does you more good than you might at first think. At the same time you won't know exactly what you are capable of doing unless you really stretch yourself, and that's something that you are not always willing to do.

You do function best from within loving relationships, and

although you can be very passionate, once you have given your heart you don't tend to change your mind readily. Personal and domestic contentment are worth a great deal to you because they represent the platform upon which you build the rest of your life. You don't make a good itinerant and probably won't indulge in travel for its own sake. Of course it does you good to get around, since anything that broadens your horizons has got to be an advantage, but you'll probably always maintain a solid home base and relish the prospect of coming back to it as frequently as possible.

Most Taureans are family people. You can be a capable parent, though tend to be a little more authoritarian than some types. Keeping an ordered sort of life is at the base of your psychology, so that even when you are young and less tidy-minded there is always a basic desire for self-discipline. This often extends to your work, where you are extremely capable and can quite easily work under your own supervision. You recognise the beautiful in all spheres of life and tend to gravitate towards clean and sanitary surroundings.

In matters of health you tend to be fairly robust, though you can suffer somewhat with headaches, often brought about as a result of a stiff neck and stress. This latter is what you should avoid as much as possible. Saying what you feel, and listening carefully to the responses, is definitely of great importance. The more you learn, the wiser you become. This makes you the natural resort of others when they need help and advice. If you try not to underestimate your own abilities, you can rise as far in life as the world at large thinks you are capable of doing. At the end of the day it is important to recognise your popularity. In all probability your friends have a much higher opinion of you than the one you cultivate for yourself.

TAURUS ON THE CUSP

Old Moore is often asked how astrological profiles are altered for those people born at either the beginning or the end of a zodiac sign, or, more properly, on the cusps of a sign. In the case of Taurus this would be on the 21st of April and for two or three days after, and similarly at the end of the sign, probably from the 18th to the 21st of May. In this year's Astral Diaries, once again, Old Moore sets out to explain the differences regarding cuspid signs.

The Aries Cusp – April 21st to April 24th

Although you have all the refinement, breeding and creative flair of the true Taurean, you are definitely more of a go-getter. Knowing what you want from life there is a slight possibility that you might be accused of being bossy and sometimes this slightly hurts your Taurean sensitivity. You have plenty of energy to get through the things that you see as being important but it is quite possible that those around you don't always see things in the same light, and this can be annoying to you. Like the typical Taurean you have great reserves of energy and can work long and hard towards any particular objective although, because Aries is also in attendance, you may push yourself slightly harder than is strictly necessary. Your temper is variable and you may not always display the typical Taurean patience with those around you.

It is possible for Taurus to 'wait in the wings' deliberately and therefore to lose out on some of the most important potential gains as a result. In your case, this is much less likely. You don't worry too much about speaking your mind. You are loving and kind, but even family members know that they will only be able to push you so far.

At work, you are capable and have executive ability. Like the Taurean you don't really care for getting your hands dirty, but if needs must you can pitch in with the best of them and enjoy a challenge. You don't worry as much as some of your Taurean friends do, but all the same you regularly expect too much of your nervous system and need frequent periods of rest.

Try not to impose your will on those around you and be content to allow things to happen on their own sometimes. This might not be an easy thing for the Aries-cusp Taurean but it's one of the sure ways to success. Confidence isn't lacking and neither is basic patience, but they do have to be encouraged and nurtured.

The Gemini Cusp – May 18th to May 21st

Oh, what a happy person you are – and how much the world loves you for it! This is definitely the more potentially fortunate of the two Taurean cusps, or at least that is how the majority of the people who know you would view it. The fact is that you are bright and breezy, easygoing and sometimes fickle on occasions, but supporting these trends is a patient, generally contented attitude to life that is both refreshing and inspiring. Getting others on your side is not hard and you have plenty of energy when it is needed the most. All the same you are quite capable of dozing in the sun occasionally and probably put far less stress on your nervous system than either Taurus or Gemini when taken alone.

You don't care too much for routines and you love variety, but yet you retain the creative and artistic qualities that come with the sign of the Bull. You work well and with confidence, but would be very likely to change direction in your career at some stage in your life and are not half so tied to routine as is usually the case for Taurus. With a friendly, and even a passionate, approach to matters of the heart you are an attentive lover and a fond parent. Most people know what you really are because you are only too willing to show them. Working out the true motivations that lurk within your soul is part of your personal search to know 'self' and is extremely important.

All in all, you have exactly what it takes to get on in life and a sense of joy and fun that makes you good to know. Patience balances your need to 'get going', whilst your mischievous streak lightens the load of the sign of Taurus which can, on occasions, take itself rather more seriously than it should.

There are many ways of coping with the requirements of life and, at one time or another, it is likely that you will try them all out. But above and beyond your need to experiment you know what is most important to you and that will always be your ultimate goal. What matters the most is your smile, which is enduring and even alluring.

TAURUS AND ITS ASCENDANTS

The nature of every individual on the planet is composed of the rich variety of zodiac signs and planetary positions that were present at the time of their birth. Your Sun sign, which in your case is Taurus, is one of the many factors when it comes to assessing the unique person you are. Probably the most important consideration, other than your Sun sign, is to establish the zodiac sign that was rising over the eastern horizon at the time that you were born. This is your Ascending or Rising sign. Most popular astrology fails to take account of the Ascendant, and yet its importance remains with you from the very moment of your birth, through every day of your life. The Ascendant is evident in the way you approach the world, and so, when meeting a person for the first time, it is this astrological influence that you are most likely to notice first. Our Ascending sign essentially represents what we appear to be, while the Sun sign is what we feel inside ourselves.

The Ascendant also has the potential for modifying our overall nature. For example, if you were born at a time of day when Taurus was passing over the eastern horizon (this would be around the time of dawn) then you would be classed as a double Taurus. As such, you would typify this zodiac sign, both internally and in your dealings with others. However, if your Ascendant sign turned out to be a Fire sign, such as Leo, there would be a profound alteration of nature, away from the expected qualities of Taurus.

One of the reasons why popular astrology often ignores the Ascendant is that it has always been rather difficult to establish. Old Moore has found a way to make this possible by devising an easy-to-use table, which you will find on page 125 of this book. Using this, you can establish your Ascendant sign at a glance. You will need to know your rough time of birth, then it is simply a case of following the instructions.

For those readers who have no idea of their time of birth it might be worth allowing a good friend, or perhaps your partner, to read through the section that follows this introduction. Someone who deals with you on a regular basis may easily discover your Ascending sign, even though you could have some difficulty establishing it for yourself. A good understanding of this component of your nature is essential if you want to be aware of that 'other person' who is responsible for the way you make contact with the world at large. Your Sun sign, Ascendant sign, and the other pointers in this book will, together, allow you a far better understanding of what makes you tick as an individual. Peeling back the different layers of your astrological make-up can be an enlightening experience, and the Ascendant may represent one of the most important layers of all.

Taurus with Taurus Ascendant

The world would see you as being fairly typical of the sign of Taurus, so you are careful, sensitive, well bred and, if other astrological trends agree, very creative. Nothing pleases you more than a tidy environment to live in and a peaceful life. You probably believe that there is a place for everything and will do your best to keep it all where it should be. It's a pity that this sometimes includes people, and you are certain to get rather irritated if they don't behave in the way that you would expect. Despite this, you are generally understanding and are very capable of giving and receiving affection.

Not everyone knows the real you, however, and it is sometimes difficult to tell the world those most personal details that can be locked deep inside. At an emotional level you tend to idealise love somewhat, though if anything this presents itself to the world as a slight 'coldness' on occasions. This is far from the truth, but your tidy mind demands that even the most intimate processes are subjected to the same sense of order with which you view the world at large. Unlike many sign combinations, you don't really rely on the help and support of others because you are more than capable yourself. In the main you live a happy life and have the ability to pass on this trait to those you care for.

Taurus with Gemini Ascendant

This is a generally happy combination which finds you better able to externalise the cultured and creative qualities which are inherent in your Taurean nature. You love to be around interesting and stimulating people and tend to be much more talkative than the typical Taurean is expected to be. The reason why Gemini helps here is because it lightens the load somewhat. Taurus is not the most introspective sign of the zodiac, but it does have that quality, and a good dose of Gemini allows you to speak your mind more freely and, as a result, to know yourself better too.

Although your mind tends to be fairly logical, you also enjoy flashes of insight that can cause you to behave in a less rational way from time to time. This is probably no bad thing because life will never be boring with you around. You try to convince yourself that you take on board all the many and varied opinions that come back at you from others, though there is a slight danger of intellectual snobbery if the responses you get are not the expected ones. You particularly like clean houses, funny people and probably fast cars. Financial rewards can come thick and fast to the Gemini-Ascendant Taurean when the logical but inspirational mind is harnessed to practical matters.

Taurus with Cancer Ascendant

Your main aim in life seems to be to look after everyone and everything that you come across. From your deepest and most enduring human love, right down to the birds in the park, you really do care and you show that natural affection in a thousand different ways. Your nature is sensitive and you are easily moved to tears, though this does not prevent you from pitching in and doing practical things to assist at just about any level. There is a danger that you could stifle those same people whom you set out to assist, and people with this zodiac combination are often unwilling, or unable, to allow their children to grow and leave the nest. More time spent considering what suits you would be no bad thing, but the problem is that you find it almost impossible to imagine any situation that doesn't involve your most basic need, which is to nurture.

You appear not to possess a selfish streak, though it sometimes turns out that, in being certain that you understand the needs and wants of the world, you are nevertheless treading on their toes. This eventual realisation can be very painful, but it isn't a stick with which you should beat yourself because at heart you are one of the kindest people imaginable. Your sense of fair play means that you are a quiet social reformer at heart.

Taurus with Leo Ascendant

Oh dear, this can be rather a hedonistic combination. The trouble is that Taurus tends to have a great sense of what looks and feels right, whilst Leo, being a Cat, is inclined to preen itself on almost any occasion. The combination tends towards self-love, which is all too likely for someone who is perfect. But don't be too dispirited about these facts because there is a great deal going for you in other ways. For a start you have one of the warmest hearts to be found anywhere and you are so brave that others marvel at the courage you display. The mountains that you climb may not be of the large, rocky sort, but you manage to find plenty of pinnacles to scale all the same, and you invariably get to the top.

Routines might bore you a little more than would be the case with Taurus alone, but you don't mind being alone. Why should you? You are probably the nicest person you know! Thus if you were ever to be cast up on a deserted island you would people the place all on your own, and there would never be any crime, untidiness or arguments. Problems only arise when other people are involved. However, in social settings you are charming, good to know and full of ideas that really have legs. You preserve your youth well into middle age, but at base you can tend to worry more than is good for you.

Taurus with Virgo Ascendant

This combination tends to amplify the Taurean qualities that you naturally possess and this is the case because both Taurus and Virgo are Earth signs. However, there are certain factors related to Virgo that show themselves very differently than the sign's cousin Taurus. Virgo is more fussy, nervy and pedantic than Taurus and all of these qualities are going to show up in your nature at one level or another. On the plus side, you might be slightly less concerned about having a perfect home and a perfect family, and your interest in life appears at a more direct level than that of the true Taurean. You care very much about your home and family and are very loyal to your friends. It's true that you sometimes tend to try and take them over, and you can also show a marked tendency to dominate, but your heart is in the right place, and most people recognise that your caring is genuine.

One problem is that there are very few shades of grey in your life, which is certainly not the case for other zodiac sign combinations.

Living your life in the way that you do, there isn't much room for compromise, and this fact alone can prove to be something of a problem where relationships are concerned. In a personal sense you need a partner who is willing to be organised and one who relies heavily on your judgements, which don't change very often.

Taurus with Libra Ascendant

A fortunate combination in many ways, this is a double Venus rulership, since both Taurus and Libra are heavily reliant on the planet of love. You are social, amiable and a natural diplomat, anxious to please and ready to care for just about anyone who shows interest in you. You hate disorder, which means that there is a place for everything and everything in its place. This can throw up the odd paradox, however, since being half Libran you cannot always work out where that place ought to be! You deal with life in a humorous way and are quite capable of seeing the absurd in yourself, as well as in others. Your heart is no bigger than that of the dyed-in-the-wool Taurean, but it sits rather closer to the surface and so others recognise it more.

On those occasions when you know you are standing on firm ground you can show great confidence, even if you have to be ready to change some of your opinions at the drop of a hat. When this happens you can be quite at odds with yourself, because Taurus doesn't take very many U-turns, whereas Libra does. Don't expect to know yourself too well, and keep looking for the funny side of things, because it is within humour that you forge the sort of life that suits you best.

Taurus with Scorpio Ascendant

The first, last and most important piece of advice for you is not to take yourself, or anyone else, too seriously. This might be rather a tall order because Scorpio intensifies the deeper qualities of Taurus and can make you rather lacking in the sense of humour that we all need to live our lives in this most imperfect of worlds. You are naturally sensuous by nature. This shows itself in a host of ways. In all probability you can spend hours in the bath, love to treat yourself to good food and drink and take your greatest pleasure in neat and orderly surroundings. On occasions this can alienate you from those who live in the same house, because other people do need to use the bathroom from time to time, and they cannot remain tidy indefinitely.

You tend to worry a great deal about things which are really not very important, but don't take this statement too seriously or you will begin to worry about this, too! You often need to lighten up and should always do your best to tell yourself that most things are not half so important as they seem to be. Be careful over the selection of a life partner and if possible choose someone who is naturally funny and who does not take life anywhere near as seriously as you are inclined to do. At work you are more than capable and in all probability everyone relies heavily on your wise judgements.

Taurus with Sagittarius Ascendant

A dual nature is evident here, and if it doesn't serve to confuse you, it will certainly be a cause of concern to many of the people with whom you share your life. You like to have a good time and are a natural party-goer. On such occasions you are accommodating, chatty and good to know. But contrast this with the quieter side of Taurus, which is directly opposed to your Sagittarian qualities. The opposition of forces is easy for you to deal with because you inhabit your own body and mind all the time, but it's far less easy for friends and relatives to understand. So on those occasions when you decide that, socially speaking, enough is enough, you may have trouble explaining this to the twelve people who are waiting outside your door with party hats and whoopee cushions.

Confidence to do almost anything is not far from the forefront of your mind and you readily embark on adventures that would have some types flapping about in horror. Here again, it is important to realise that we are not all built the same way and that gentle coaxing is sometimes necessary to bring others round to your point of view. If you really have a fault it could be that you are so busy being your own, rather less than predictable self, that you fail to take the rest of the world into account.

Taurus with Capricorn Ascendant

It might appear on the surface that you are not the most interesting person in the world. This is a pity, for you have an active though very logical mind, so logical in some instances that you would have a great deal in common with Mr Spock. This is the thorn in your flesh, or rather the flesh of everyone else, since you are probably quite happy being exactly what you are. You can think things through in a clear and very practical way and end up taking decisions that are balanced, eminently sensible, but, on occasions, rather dull.

Actually there is a fun machine somewhere deep within that Earthsign nature and those who know you the best will recognise the fact. Often this combination is attended by a deep and biting sense of humour, but it's of the sort that less intelligent and considered types would find rather difficult to recognise. It is likely that you have no lack of confidence in your own judgement and you have all the attributes necessary to do very well on the financial front. Slow and steady progress is your way and you need to be quite certain before you commit yourself to any new venture. This is a zodiac combination that can soak up years of stress and numerous difficulties, yet still come out on top. Nothing holds you back for long and you tend to be very brave.

Taurus with Aquarius Ascendant

There is nothing that you fail to think about deeply and with great intensity. You are wise, honest and very scientific in your approach to life. Routines are necessary in life, but you have most of them sorted out well in advance and so always have time to look at the next interesting fact. If you don't spend all your time watching documentaries on the television set, you make a good friend and love to socialise. Most of the great discoveries of the world were probably made by people with this sort of astrological combination, though your nature is rather 'odd' on occasions and so can be rather difficult for others to understand.

You may be most surprised when others tell you that you are eccentric, but you don't really mind too much because for half of the time you are not inhabiting the same world as the rest of us. Because you can be delightfully dotty you are probably much loved and cherished by your friends, of which there are likely to be many. Family members probably adore you too and you can be guaranteed to entertain anyone with whom you come into contact. The only fly in the ointment is that you sometimes lose track of reality, whatever that might be, and fly high in your own atmosphere of rarefied possibilities.

Taurus with Pisces Ascendant

You are clearly a very sensitive type of person and that sometimes makes it rather difficult for others to know how they might best approach you. Private and deep, you are nevertheless socially inclined on many occasions. However, because your nature is bottomless it is possible that some types would actually accuse you of being shallow. How can this come about? Well, it's simple really. The fact is that you rarely show anyone what is going on in the deepest recesses of your mind and so your responses can appear to be trite or even ill-considered. This is far from the truth, as those who are allowed into the 'inner sanctum' would readily admit. You are something of a sensualist, and relish staying in bed late and simply pleasing yourself for days on end. However, you are a Taurean at heart so you desire a tidy environment in which to live your usually long life.

You are able to deal with the routine aspects of life quite well and can be a capable worker once you are up and firing on all cylinders. It is very important that you maintain an interest in what you are doing because the recesses of your dreamy mind can sometimes appear to be infinitely more attractive. Your imagination is second to none and this fact can often be turned to your advantage.

Taurus with Aries Ascendant

This is a steady combination, so much so that even experienced astrologers would be unlikely to recognise that the Aries quality is present at all, unless of course they came to know you very well. Your approach to life tends to be slow and considered and there is a great danger that you could suppress those feelings that others of your kind would be only too willing to verbalise. To compensate, you are deeply creative and will think matters through much more readily than more dominant Aries types would be inclined to do. In your dealings with the world, you are, nevertheless, somewhat locked inside yourself and can struggle to achieve the level of communication that you so desperately need. Frustration might follow, were it not for the fact that you possess a quiet determination that, to those in the know, is the clearest window through to your Taurean soul.

The care for others is strong and you certainly demonstrate this at all levels. The fact is that you live a great percentage of your life in service to the people you take to, whilst at the same time being able to shut the door firmly in the face of people who irritate or anger you. You are deeply motivated towards family relationships.

THE MOON AND THE PART IT PLAYS IN YOUR LIFE

In astrology the Moon is probably the single most important heavenly body after the Sun. Its unique position, as partner to the Earth on its journey around the solar system, means that the Moon appears to pass through the signs of the zodiac extremely quickly. The zodiac position of the Moon at the time of your birth plays a great part in personal character and is especially significant in the build-up of your emotional nature.

Sun Moon Cycles

The first lunar cycle deals with the part the position of the Moon plays relative to your Sun sign. I have made the fluctuations of this pattern easy for you to understand by means of a simple cyclic graph. It appears on the first page of each 'Your Month At A Glance', under the title 'Highs and Lows'. The graph displays the lunar cycle and you will soon learn to understand how its movements have a bearing on your level of energy and your abilities.

Your Own Moon Sign

Discovering the position of the Moon at the time of your birth has always been notoriously difficult because tracking the complex zodiac positions of the Moon is not easy. This process has been reduced to three simple stages with Old Moore's unique Lunar Tables. A breakdown of the Moon's zodiac positions can be found from page 28 onwards, so that once you know what your Moon Sign is, you can see what part this plays in the overall build-up of your personal character.

If you follow the instructions on the next page you will soon be able to work out exactly what zodiac sign the Moon occupied on the day that you were born and you can then go on to compare the reading for this position with those of your Sun sign and your Ascendant. It is partly the comparison between these three important positions that goes towards making you the unique individual you are.

HOW TO DISCOVER YOUR MOON SIGN

This is a three-stage process. You may need a pen and a piece of paper but if you follow the instructions below the process should only take a minute or so.

STAGE 1 First of all you need to know the Moon Age at the time of your birth. If you look at Moon Table 1, on page 26, you will find all the years between 1920 and 2018 down the left side. Find the year of your birth and then trace across to the right to the month of your birth. Where the two intersect you will find a number. This is the date of the New Moon in the month that you were born. You now need to count forward the number of days between the New Moon and your own birthday. For example, if the New Moon in the month of your birth was shown as being the 6th and you were born on the 20th, your Moon Age Day would be 14. If the New Moon in the month of your birth came after your birthday, you need to count forward from the New Moon in the previous month. If you were born in a Leap Year, remember to count the 29th February. You can tell if your birth year was a Leap Year if the last two digits can be divided by four. Whatever the result, jot this number down so that you do not forget it.

STAGE 2 Take a look at Moon Table 2 on page 27. Down the left hand column look for the date of your birth. Now trace across to the month of your birth. Where the two meet you will find a letter. Copy this letter down alongside your Moon Age Day.

STAGE 3 Moon Table 3 on page 27 will supply you with the zodiac sign the Moon occupied on the day of your birth. Look for your Moon Age Day down the left hand column and then for the letter you found in Stage 2. Where the two converge you will find a zodiac sign and this is the sign occupied by the Moon on the day that you were born.

Your Zodiac Moon Sign Explained

You will find a profile of all zodiac Moon Signs on pages 28 to 31, showing in yet another way how astrology helps to make you into the individual that you are. In each daily entry of the Astral Diary you can find the zodiac position of the Moon for every day of the year. This also allows you to discover your lunar birthdays. Since the Moon passes through all the signs of the zodiac in about a month, you can expect something like twelve lunar birthdays each year. At these times you are likely to be emotionally steady and able to make the sort of decisions that have real, lasting value.

Moon Table 1

YEAR	MAR	APR	MAY	YEAR	MAR	APR	MAY	YEAR	MAR	APR	MAY
1920	20	18	18	1953	15	13	13	1986	10	9	8
1921	9	8	7	1954	5	3	2	1987	29	28	27
1922	28	27	26	1955	24	22	21	1988	18	16	15
1923	17	16	15	1956	12	11	10	1989	7	6	5
1924	5	4	3	1957	1/31	29	29	1990	26	25	24
1925	24	23	22	1958	20	19	18	1991	15	13	13
1926	14	12	11	1959	9	8	7	1992	4	3	2
1927	3	2	1/30	1960	27	26	26	1993	24	22	21
1928	21	20	19	1961	16	15	14	1994	12	11	10
1929	11	9	9	1962	6	5	4	1995	30	29	29
1930	30	28	28	1963	25	23	23	1996	19	18	18
1931	19	18	17	1964	14	12	11	1997	9	7	6
1932	7	6	5	1965	2	1	1/30	1998	27	26	25
1933	26	24	24	1966	21	20	19	1999	17	16	15
1934	15	13	13	1967	10	9	8	2000	6	4	4
1935	5	3	2	1968	29	28	27	2001	24	23	22
1936	23	21	20	1969	18	16	15	2002	13	12	10
1937	13	12	10	1970	7	6	6	2003	2	1	1/30
1938	2/31	30	29	1971	26	25	24	2004	21	19	18
1939	20	19	19	1972	15	13	13	2005	10	8	8
1940	9	7	7	1973	5	3	2	2006	29	27	27
1941	27	26	26	1974	24	22	21	2007	18	17	15
1942	16	15	15	1975	12	11	11	2008	7	6	5
1943	6	4	4	1976	30	29	29	2009	26	25	24
1944	24	22	22	1977	19	18	18	2010	15	14	14
1945	14	12	11	1978	9	7	7	2011	5	3	3
1946	3	2	1/30	1979	27	26	26	2012	22	21	20
1947	21	20	19	1980	16	15	14	2013	12	10	10
1948	11	9	9	1981	6	4	4	2014	1/31	30	29
1949	29	28	27	1982	24	23	21	2015	20	19	18
1950	18	17	17	1983	14	13	12	2016	8	7	8
1951	7	6	6	1984	2	1	1/30	2017	27	25	25
1952	25	24	23	1985	21	20	19	2018	17	16	15

Table 2

DAY	APR	MAY
1	J	M
2	J	M
3	J	M
4	J	M
5	J	M
6	J	M
7	J	M
8	J	M
9	J	M
10	J	M
11	K	M
12	K	N
13	K	N
14	K	N
15	K	N
16	K	N
17	K	N
18	K	N
19	K	N
20	K	N
21	L	N
22	L	O
23	L	O
24	L	O
25	L	O
26	L	O
27	L	O
28	L	O
29	L	O
30	L	O
31	–	O

Table 3

M/D	J	K	L	M	N	O	P
0	AR	TA	TA	TA	GE	GE	GE
1	TA	TA	TA	GE	GE	GE	CA
2	TA	TA	GE	GE	GE	CA	CA
3	TA	GE	GE	GE	CA	CA	CA
4	GE	GE	GE	CA	CA	CA	LE
5	GE	CA	CA	CA	LE	LE	LE
6	CA	CA	CA	LE	LE	LE	VI
7	CA	CA	LE	LE	LE	VI	VI
8	CA	LE	LE	LE	VI	VI	VI
9	LE	LE	VI	VI	VI	LI	LI
10	LE	VI	VI	VI	LI	LI	LI
11	VI	VI	VI	LI	LI	SC	SC
12	VI	VI	LI	LI	LI	SC	SC
13	VI	LI	LI	LI	SC	SC	SC
14	LI	LI	LI	SC	SC	SA	SA
15	LI	SC	SC	SC	SA	SA	SA
16	SC	SC	SC	SA	SA	SA	CP
17	SC	SC	SA	SA	SA	CP	CP
18	SC	SA	SA	SA	CP	CP	CP
19	SA	SA	SA	CP	CP	CP	AQ
20	SA	CP	CP	CP	AQ	AQ	AQ
21	CP	CP	CP	AQ	AQ	AQ	PI
22	CP	CP	AQ	AQ	AQ	PI	PI
23	CP	AQ	AQ	AQ	PI	PI	PI
24	AQ	AQ	AQ	PI	PI	PI	AR
25	AQ	PI	PI	PI	AR	AR	AR
26	PI	PI	PI	AR	AR	AR	TA
27	PI	PI	AR	AR	AR	TA	TA
28	PI	AR	AR	AR	TA	TA	TA
29	AR	AR	AR	TA	TA	TA	GE

AR = Aries, TA = Taurus, GE = Gemini, CA = Cancer, LE = Leo, VI = Virgo, LI = Libra, SC = Scorpio, SA = Sagittarius, CP = Capricorn, AQ = Aquarius, PI = Pisces

MOON SIGNS

Moon in Aries

You have a strong imagination, courage, determination and a desire to do things in your own way and forge your own path through life.

Originality is a key attribute; you are seldom stuck for ideas although your mind is changeable and you could take the time to focus on individual tasks. Often quick-tempered, you take orders from few people and live life at a fast pace. Avoid health problems by taking regular time out for rest and relaxation.

Emotionally, it is important that you talk to those you are closest to and work out your true feelings. Once you discover that people are there to help, there is less necessity for you to do everything yourself.

Moon in Taurus

The Moon in Taurus gives you a courteous and friendly manner, which means you are likely to have many friends.

The good things in life mean a lot to you, as Taurus is an Earth sign that delights in experiences which please the senses. Hence you are probably a lover of good food and drink, which may in turn mean you need to keep an eye on the bathroom scales, especially as looking good is also important to you.

Emotionally you are fairly stable and you stick by your own standards. Taureans do not respond well to change. Intuition also plays an important part in your life.

Moon in Gemini

You have a warm-hearted character, sympathetic and eager to help others. At times reserved, you can also be articulate and chatty: this is part of the paradox of Gemini, which always brings duplicity to the nature. You are interested in current affairs, have a good intellect, and are good company and likely to have many friends. Most of your friends have a high opinion of you and would be ready to defend you should the need arise. However, this is usually unnecessary, as you are quite capable of defending yourself in any verbal confrontation.

Travel is important to your inquisitive mind and you find intellectual stimulus in mixing with people from different cultures. You also gain much from reading, writing and the arts but you do need plenty of rest and relaxation in order to avoid fatigue.

Moon in Cancer

The Moon in Cancer at the time of birth is a fortunate position as Cancer is the Moon's natural home. This means that the qualities of compassion and understanding given by the Moon are especially enhanced in your nature, and you are friendly and sociable and cope well with emotional pressures. You cherish home and family life, and happily do the domestic tasks. Your surroundings are important to you and you hate squalor and filth. You are likely to have a love of music and poetry.

Your basic character, although at times changeable like the Moon itself, depends on symmetry. You aim to make your surroundings comfortable and harmonious, for yourself and those close to you.

Moon in Leo

The best qualities of the Moon and Leo come together to make you warmhearted, fair, ambitious and self-confident. With good organisational abilities, you invariably rise to a position of responsibility in your chosen career. This is fortunate as you don't enjoy being an 'also-ran' and would rather be an important part of a small organisation than a menial in a large one.

You should be lucky in love, and happy, provided you put in the effort to make a comfortable home for yourself and those close to you. It is likely that you will have a love of pleasure, sport, music and literature. Life brings you many rewards, most of them as a direct result of your own efforts, although you may be luckier than average and ready to make the best of any situation.

Moon in Virgo

You are endowed with good mental abilities and a keen receptive memory, but you are never ostentatious or pretentious. Naturally quite reserved, you still have many friends, especially of the opposite sex. Marital relationships must be discussed carefully and worked at so that they remain harmonious, as personal attachments can be a problem if you do not give them your full attention.

Talented and persevering, you possess artistic qualities and are a good homemaker. Earning your honours through genuine merit, you work long and hard towards your objectives but show little pride in your achievements. Many short journeys will be undertaken in your life.

Moon in Libra

With the Moon in Libra you are naturally popular and make friends easily. People like you, probably more than you realise, you bring fun to a party and are a natural diplomat. For all its good points, Libra is not the most stable of astrological signs and, as a result, your emotions can be a little unstable too. Therefore, although the Moon in Libra is said to be good for love and marriage, your Sun sign and Rising sign will have an important effect on your emotional and loving qualities.

You must remember to relate to others in your decision-making. Co-operation is crucial because Libra represents the 'balance' of life that can only be achieved through harmonious relationships. Conformity is not easy for you because Libra, an Air sign, likes its independence.

Moon in Scorpio

Some people might call you pushy. In fact, all you really want to do is to live life to the full and protect yourself and your family from the pressures of life. Take care to avoid giving the impression of being sarcastic or impulsive and use your energies wisely and constructively.

You have great courage and you invariably achieve your goals by force of personality and sheer effort. You are fond of mystery and are good at predicting the outcome of situations and events. Travel experiences can be beneficial to you.

You may experience problems if you do not take time to examine your motives in a relationship, and also if you allow jealousy, always a feature of Scorpio, to cloud your judgement.

Moon in Sagittarius

The Moon in Sagittarius helps to make you a generous individual with humanitarian qualities and a kind heart. Restlessness may be intrinsic as your mind is seldom still. Perhaps because of this, you have a need for change that could lead you to several major moves during your adult life. You are not afraid to stand your ground when you know your judgement is right, you speak directly and have good intuition.

At work you are quick, efficient and versatile and so you make an ideal employee. You need work to be intellectually demanding and do not enjoy tedious routines.

In relationships, you anger quickly if faced with stupidity or deception, though you are just as quick to forgive and forget. Emotionally, there are times when your heart rules your head.

Moon in Capricorn

The Moon in Capricorn makes you popular and likely to come into the public eye in some way. The watery Moon is not entirely comfortable in the Earth sign of Capricorn and this may lead to some difficulties in the early years of life. An initial lack of creative ability and indecision must be overcome before the true qualities of patience and perseverance inherent in Capricorn can show through.

You have good administrative ability and are a capable worker, and if you are careful you can accumulate wealth. But you must be cautious and take professional advice in partnerships, as you are open to deception. You may be interested in social or welfare work, which suit your organisational skills and sympathy for others.

Moon in Aquarius

The Moon in Aquarius makes you an active and agreeable person with a friendly, easy-going nature. Sympathetic to the needs of others, you flourish in a laid-back atmosphere. You are broad-minded, fair and open to suggestion, although sometimes you have an unconventional quality which others can find hard to understand.

You are interested in the strange and curious, and in old articles and places. You enjoy trips to these places and gain much from them. Political, scientific and educational work interests you and you might choose a career in science or technology.

Money-wise, you make gains through innovation and concentration and Lunar Aquarians often tackle more than one job at a time. In love you are kind and honest.

Moon in Pisces

You have a kind, sympathetic nature, somewhat retiring at times, but you always take account of others' feelings and help when you can.

Personal relationships may be problematic, but as life goes on you can learn from your experiences and develop a better understanding of yourself and the world around you.

You have a fondness for travel, appreciate beauty and harmony and hate disorder and strife. You may be fond of literature and would make a good writer or speaker yourself. You have a creative imagination and may come across as an incurable romantic. You have strong intuition, maybe bordering on a mediumistic quality, which sets you apart from the mass. You may not be rich in cash terms, but your personal gifts are worth more than gold.

TAURUS IN LOVE

Discover how compatible you are with people from the same and other signs of the zodiac. Five stars equals a match made in heaven!

Taurus meets Taurus

A certainty for complete success or absolute failure. Taurus has enough self-knowledge to recognise the strengths of a fellow Taurean, so these two can live in harmony. Both will be tidy and live in comfortable surroundings. Two Taureans seldom argue and will be good friends. But something may be lacking – a spark that doesn't ignite. Passion is important and Taurus reflects, rather than creates it. The prognosis is good, but someone must turn the heat up to get things really cooking. Star rating: ****

Taurus meets Gemini

Gemini people can infuriate the generally steady Taurean nature as they are so untidy, which is a complete reversal of the Taurean ethos. At first this won't matter; Mr or Miss Gemini is enchanting, entertaining and very different. But time will tell, and that's why this potential relationship only has two stars. There is hope, however, because Taurus can curb some of the excesses of the Twins, whilst Gemini is capable of preventing the Bull from taking itself too seriously. Star rating: **

Taurus meets Cancer

This pair will have the tidiest house in the street – every stick of furniture in place, and no errant blade of grass daring to spoil the lawn. But things inside the relationship might not be quite so ship-shape as both signs need, but don't offer, encouragement. There's plenty of affection, but few incentives for mutual progress. This might not prevent material success, but an enduring relationship isn't based on money alone. Passion is essential, and both parties need to realise and aim for that. Star rating: **

Taurus meets Leo

Here we find a generally successful pairing, which frequently leads to an enduring relationship. Taurus needs stimulation which Leo is happy to offer, while Leo responds well to the Bull's sense of order. The essence of the relationship is balance, but it may be achieved with wild swings of the scales on the way, so don't expect a quiet life, though this pair will enjoy a reconciliation after an argument! Material success is probable and, as both like children, a family is likely. Star rating: ***

Taurus meets Virgo

This is a difficult basis for a successful relationship, and yet it often works. Both signs are from the Earth element, so have a common-sense approach to life. They have a mutual understanding, and share many interests. Taurus understands and copes well with Virgo's fussy nature, while Virgo revels in the Bull's tidy and artistic qualities. Both sides are committed to achieving lasting material success. There won't be fireworks, and the match may lack a certain 'spiritual' feel, but as that works both ways it may not be a problem. Star rating: *****

Taurus meets Libra

A happy life is important to both these signs and, as they are both ruled by Venus, they share a common understanding, even though they display themselves so differently. Taurus is quieter than Libra, but can be decisive, and that's what counts. Libra is interested in absolutely everything, an infectious quality when seen through Taurean eyes. The slightly flighty qualities of Libra may lead to jealousy from the Bull. Not an argumentative relationship and one that often works well. There could be many changes of address for this pair. Star rating: ****

Taurus meets Scorpio

Scorpio is deep – very deep – which may be a problem, because Taurus doesn't wear its heart on its sleeve either. It might be difficult for this pair to get together, because neither are naturally inclined to make the first move. Taurus stands in awe of the power and intensity of the Scorpio mind, while the Scorpion is interested in the Bull's affable and friendly qualities, so an enduring relationship could be forged if the couple ever get round to talking. Both are lovers of home and family, which will help to cement a relationship. Star rating: **

Taurus meets Sagittarius

On first impression, Taurus may not like Sagittarius, who may seem brash, and even common, when viewed through the Bull's refined eyes. But there is hope of success because the two signs have so much to offer each other. The Archer is enthralled by the Taurean's natural poise and beauty, while Taurus always needs more basic confidence, which is no problem to Sagittarius who has plenty to spare. Both signs love to travel. There are certain to be ups and downs, but that doesn't prevent an interesting, inspiring and even exciting combination. Star rating: ***

Taurus meets Capricorn

If not quite a match made in heaven, this comes close. Both signs are earthy in nature and that is a promising start. Capricorn is very practical and can make a Taurean's dreams come true. Both are tidy, like to know what is going to happen in a day-to-day sense, and are steady and committed. Taurus loves refinement, which Capricorn accepts and even helps to create. A good prognosis for material success rounds off a relationship that could easily stay the course. The only thing missing is a genuine sense of humour. Star rating: *****

Taurus meets Aquarius

In any relationship of which Aquarius is a part, surprises abound. It is difficult for Taurus to understand the soul-searching, adventurous, changeable Aquarian, but on the positive side, the Bull is adaptable and can respond well to a dose of excitement. Aquarians are kind and react well to the same quality coming back at them. Both are friendly, capable of deep affection and basically quite creative. Unfortunately, though, Taurus simply doesn't know what makes Aquarius tick, which could lead to hidden feelings of isolation. Star rating: **

Taurus meets Pisces

No problem here, unless both parties come from the quieter side of their respective signs. Most of the time Taurus and Pisces would live comfortably together, offering mutual support and deep regard. Taurus can offer the personal qualities that Pisces craves, whilst Pisces understands and copes with the Bull's slightly stubborn qualities. Taurus is likely to travel in Piscean company, so there is a potential for wide-ranging experiences and variety which is essential. There will be some misunderstandings, mainly because Pisces is so deep, but that won't prevent their enduring happiness. Star rating: ***

Taurus meets Aries

This match has been known to work very well. Aries brings dynamism and ambition, while Taurus has the patience to see things through logically. Such complementary views work equally well in a relationship or in an office environment. There is mutual respect, but sometimes a lack of total understanding. The romantic needs of each sign are quite different, but both are still fulfilled. Taurus and Aries can live easily in domestic harmony which is very important but, interestingly, Aries may be the loser in battles of will. Star rating: ***

VENUS:
THE PLANET OF LOVE

If you look up at the sky around sunset or sunrise you will often see Venus in close attendance to the Sun. It is arguably one of the most beautiful sights of all and there is little wonder that historically it became associated with the goddess of love. But although Venus does play an important part in the way you view love and in the way others see you romantically, this is only one of the spheres of influence that it enjoys in your overall character.

Venus has a part to play in the more cultured side of your life and has much to do with your appreciation of art, literature, music and general creativity. Even the way you look is responsive to the part of the zodiac that Venus occupied at the start of your life, though this fact is also down to your Sun sign and Ascending sign. If, at the time you were born, Venus occupied one of the more gregarious zodiac signs, you will be more likely to wear your heart on your sleeve, as well as to be more attracted to entertainment, social gatherings and good company. If on the other hand Venus occupied a quiet zodiac sign at the time of your birth, you would tend to be more retiring and less willing to shine in public situations.

It's good to know what part the planet Venus plays in your life, for it can have a great bearing on the way you appear to the rest of the world and since we all have to mix with others, you can learn to make the very best of what Venus has to offer you.

One of the great complications in the past has always been trying to establish exactly what zodiac position Venus enjoyed when you were born, because the planet is notoriously difficult to track. However, I have solved that problem by creating a table that is exclusive to your Sun sign, which you will find on the following page.

Establishing your Venus sign could not be easier. Just look up the year of your birth on the page opposite and you will see a sign of the zodiac. This was the sign that Venus occupied in the period covered by your sign in that year. If Venus occupied more than one sign during the period, this is indicated by the date on which the sign changed, and the name of the new sign. For instance, if you were born in 1950, Venus was in Pisces until the 5th May, after which time it was in Aries. If you were born before 5th May your Venus sign is Pisces, if you were born on or after 5th May, your Venus sign is Aries. Once you have established the position of Venus at the time of your birth, you can then look in the pages which follow to see how this has a bearing on your life as a whole.

1920 ARIES / 7.5 TAURUS
1921 TAURUS / 27.4 ARIES
1922 TAURUS / 2.5 GEMINI
1923 PISCES / 27.4 ARIES
1924 GEMINI / 7.5 CANCER
1925 TAURUS / 16.5 GEMINI
1926 PISCES / 6.5 ARIES
1927 GEMINI / 12.5 CANCER
1928 ARIES / 6.5 TAURUS
1929 TAURUS / 24.4 ARIES
1930 TAURUS / 1.5 GEMINI
1931 PISCES / 26.4 ARIES
1932 GEMINI / 8.5 CANCER
1933 TAURUS / 15.5 GEMINI
1934 PISCES / 6.5 ARIES
1935 GEMINI / 12.5 CANCER
1936 ARIES / 6.5 TAURUS
1937 TAURUS / 21.4 ARIES
1938 TAURUS / 1.5 GEMINI
1939 PISCES / 26.4 ARIES
1940 GEMINI / 9.5 CANCER
1941 TAURUS / 14.5 GEMINI
1942 PISCES / 6.5 ARIES
1943 GEMINI / 11.5 CANCER
1944 ARIES / 6.5 TAURUS
1945 ARIES
1946 TAURUS / 30.4 GEMINI
1947 PISCES / 25.4 ARIES
1948 GEMINI / 9.5 CANCER
1949 TAURUS / 14.5 GEMINI
1950 PISCES / 5.5 ARIES
1951 GEMINI / 11.5 CANCER
1952 ARIES / 5.5 TAURUS
1953 ARIES
1954 TAURUS / 29.4 GEMINI
1955 PISCES / 25.4 ARIES
1956 GEMINI / 10.5 CANCER
1957 TAURUS / 13.5 GEMINI
1958 PISCES / 5.5 ARIES
1959 GEMINI / 10.5 CANCER
1960 ARIES / 4.5 TAURUS
1961 ARIES
1962 TAURUS / 28.4 GEMINI
1963 PISCES / 24.4 ARIES
1964 GEMINI / 11.5 CANCER
1965 TAURUS / 13.5 GEMINI
1966 PISCES / 5.5 ARIES
1967 GEMINI / 10.5 CANCER
1968 ARIES / 4.5 TAURUS
1969 ARIES
1970 TAURUS / 27.4 GEMINI
1971 PISCES / 24.4 ARIES
1972 GEMINI / 12.5 CANCER
1973 TAURUS / 12.5 GEMINI

1974 PISCES / 4.5 ARIES
1975 GEMINI / 9.5 CANCER
1976 ARIES / 3.5 TAURUS
1977 ARIES
1978 TAURUS / 27.4 GEMINI
1979 PISCES / 23.4 ARIES
1980 GEMINI / 13.5 CANCER
1981 TAURUS / 12.5 GEMINI
1982 PISCES / 4.5 ARIES
1983 GEMINI / 9.5 CANCER
1984 ARIES / 3.5 TAURUS
1985 ARIES
1986 TAURUS / 26.4 GEMINI
1987 PISCES / 23.4 ARIES
1988 GEMINI / 15.5 CANCER
1989 TAURUS / 11.5 GEMINI
1990 PISCES / 4.5 ARIES
1991 GEMINI / 8.5 CANCER
1992 ARIES / 2.5 TAURUS
1993 ARIES
1994 TAURUS / 26.4 GEMINI
1995 PISCES / 22.4 ARIES
1996 GEMINI / 15.5 CANCER
1997 TAURUS / 11.5 GEMINI
1998 PISCES / 3.5 ARIES
1999 GEMINI / 8.5 CANCER
2000 ARIES / 2.5 TAURUS
2001 ARIES
2002 TAURUS / 26.4 GEMINI
2003 PISCES / 22.4 ARIES
2004 GEMINI / 15.5 CANCER
2005 TAURUS / 11.5 GEMINI
2006 PISCES / 3.5 ARIES
2007 GEMINI / 8.5 CANCER
2008 ARIES / 2.5 TAURUS
2009 ARIES
2010 TAURUS / 26.4 GEMINI
2011 PISCES / 22.4 ARIES
2012 PISCES / 22.4 ARIES
2013 PISCES / 3.5 ARIES
2014 PISCES / 3.5 ARIES
2015 GEMINI / 8.5 CANCER
2016 TAURUS
2017 GEMINI / 15.5 CANCER
2018 TAURUS / 26.4 GEMINI

VENUS THROUGH THE ZODIAC SIGNS

Venus in Aries

Amongst other things, the position of Venus in Aries indicates a fondness for travel, music and all creative pursuits. Your nature tends to be affectionate and you would try not to create confusion or difficulty for others if it could be avoided. Many people with this planetary position have a great love of the theatre, and mental stimulation is of the greatest importance. Early romantic attachments are common with Venus in Aries, so it is very important to establish a genuine sense of romantic continuity. Early marriage is not recommended, especially if it is based on sympathy. You may give your heart a little too readily on occasions.

Venus in Taurus

You are capable of very deep feelings and your emotions tend to last for a very long time. This makes you a trusting partner and lover, whose constancy is second to none. In life you are precise and careful and always try to do things the right way. Although this means an ordered life, which you are comfortable with, it can also lead you to be rather too fussy for your own good. Despite your pleasant nature, you are very fixed in your opinions and quite able to speak your mind. Others are attracted to you and historical astrologers always quoted this position of Venus as being very fortunate in terms of marriage. However, if you find yourself involved in a failed relationship, it could take you a long time to trust again.

Venus in Gemini

As with all associations related to Gemini, you tend to be quite versatile, anxious for change and intelligent in your dealings with the world at large. You may gain money from more than one source but you are equally good at spending it. There is an inference here that you are a good communicator, via either the written or the spoken word, and you love to be in the company of interesting people. Always on the look-out for culture, you may also be very fond of music, and love to indulge the curious and cultured side of your nature. In romance you tend to have more than one relationship and could find yourself associated with someone who has previously been a friend or even a distant relative.

Venus in Cancer

You often stay close to home because you are very fond of family and enjoy many of your most treasured moments when you are with those you love. Being naturally sympathetic, you will always do anything you can to support those around you, even people you hardly know at all. This charitable side of your nature is your most noticeable trait and is one of the reasons why others are naturally so fond of you. Being receptive and in some cases even psychic, you can see through to the soul of most of those with whom you come into contact. You may not commence too many romantic attachments but when you do give your heart, it tends to be unconditionally.

Venus in Leo

It must become quickly obvious to almost anyone you meet that you are kind, sympathetic and yet determined enough to stand up for anyone or anything that is truly important to you. Bright and sunny, you warm the world with your natural enthusiasm and would rarely do anything to hurt those around you, or at least not intentionally. In romance you are ardent and sincere, though some may find your style just a little overpowering. Gains come through your contacts with other people and this could be especially true with regard to romance, for love and money often come hand in hand for those who were born with Venus in Leo. People claim to understand you, though you are more complex than you seem.

Venus in Virgo

Your nature could well be fairly quiet no matter what your Sun sign might be, though this fact often manifests itself as an inner peace and would not prevent you from being basically sociable. Some delays and even the odd disappointment in love cannot be ruled out with this planetary position, though it's a fact that you will usually find the happiness you look for in the end. Catapulting yourself into romantic entanglements that you know to be rather ill-advised is not sensible, and it would be better to wait before you committed yourself exclusively to any one person. It is the essence of your nature to serve the world at large and through doing so it is possible that you will attract money at some stage in your life.

Venus in Libra

Venus is very comfortable in Libra and bestows upon those people who have this planetary position a particular sort of kindness that is easy to recognise. This is a very good position for all sorts of friendships and also for romantic attachments that usually bring much joy into your life. Few individuals with Venus in Libra would avoid marriage and since you are capable of great depths of love, it is likely that you will find a contented personal life. You like to mix with people of integrity and intelligence but don't take kindly to scruffy surroundings or work that means getting your hands too dirty. Careful speculation, good business dealings and money through marriage all seem fairly likely.

Venus in Scorpio

You are quite open and tend to spend money quite freely, even on those occasions when you don't have very much. Although your intentions are always good, there are times when you get yourself in to the odd scrape and this can be particularly true when it comes to romance, which you may come to late or from a rather unexpected direction. Certainly you have the power to be happy and to make others contented on the way, but you find the odd stumbling block on your journey through life and it could seem that you have to work harder than those around you. As a result of this, you gain a much deeper understanding of the true value of personal happiness than many people ever do, and are likely to achieve true contentment in the end.

Venus in Sagittarius

You are lighthearted, cheerful and always able to see the funny side of any situation. These facts enhance your popularity, which is especially high with members of the opposite sex. You should never have to look too far to find romantic interest in your life, though it is just possible that you might be too willing to commit yourself before you are certain that the person in question is right for you. Part of the problem here extends to other areas of life too. The fact is that you like variety in everything and so can tire of situations that fail to offer it. All the same, if you choose wisely and learn to understand your restless side, then great happiness can be yours.

Venus in Capricorn

The most notable trait that comes from Venus in this position is that it makes you trustworthy and able to take on all sorts of responsibilities in life. People are instinctively fond of you and love you all the more because you are always ready to help those who are in any form of need. Social and business popularity can be yours and there is a magnetic quality to your nature that is particularly attractive in a romantic sense. Anyone who wants a partner for a lover, a spouse and a good friend too would almost certainly look in your direction. Constancy is the hallmark of your nature and unfaithfulness would go right against the grain. You might sometimes be a little too trusting.

Venus in Aquarius

This location of Venus offers a fondness for travel and a desire to try out something new at every possible opportunity. You are extremely easy to get along with and tend to have many friends from varied backgrounds, classes and inclinations. You like to live a distinct sort of life and gain a great deal from moving about, both in a career sense and with regard to your home. It is not out of the question that you could form a romantic attachment to someone who comes from far away or be attracted to a person of a distinctly artistic and original nature. What you cannot stand is jealousy, for you have friends of both sexes and would want to keep things that way.

Venus in Pisces

The first thing people tend to notice about you is your wonderful, warm smile. Being very charitable by nature you will do anything to help others, even if you don't know them well. Much of your life may be spent sorting out situations for other people, but it is very important to feel that you are living for yourself too. In the main, you remain cheerful, and tend to be quite attractive to members of the opposite sex. Where romantic attachments are concerned, you could be drawn to people who are significantly older or younger than yourself or to someone with a unique career or point of view. It might be best for you to avoid marrying whilst you are still very young.

HOW THE DIAGRAMS WORK

Through the picture diagrams in the Astral Diary I want to help you to plot your year. With them you can see where the positive and negative aspects will be found in each month. To make the most of them, all you have to do is remember where and when!

Let me show you how they work ...

THE MONTH AT A GLANCE

Just as there are twelve separate zodiac signs, so astrologers believe that each sign has twelve separate aspects to life. Each of the twelve segments relates to a different personal aspect. I list them all every month so that their meanings are always clear.

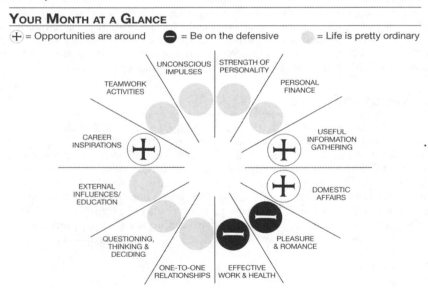

YOUR MONTH AT A GLANCE

⊕ = Opportunities are around ● = Be on the defensive ● = Life is pretty ordinary

- UNCONSCIOUS IMPULSES
- STRENGTH OF PERSONALITY
- TEAMWORK ACTIVITIES
- PERSONAL FINANCE
- CAREER INSPIRATIONS
- USEFUL INFORMATION GATHERING
- EXTERNAL INFLUENCES/ EDUCATION
- DOMESTIC AFFAIRS
- QUESTIONING, THINKING & DECIDING
- PLEASURE & ROMANCE
- ONE-TO-ONE RELATIONSHIPS
- EFFECTIVE WORK & HEALTH

I have designed this chart to show you how and when these twelve different aspects are being influenced throughout the year. When there is a shaded circle, nothing out of the ordinary is to be expected. However, when a circle turns white with a plus sign, the influence is positive. Where the circle is black with a minus sign, it is a negative.

YOUR ENERGY RHYTHM CHART

Below is a picture diagram in which I link your zodiac group to the rhythm of the Moon. In doing this I have calculated when you will be gaining strength from its influence and equally when you may be weakened by it.

If you think of yourself as being like the tides of the ocean then you may understand how your own energies must also rise and fall. And if you understand how it works and when it is working, then you can better organise your activities to achieve more and get things done more easily.

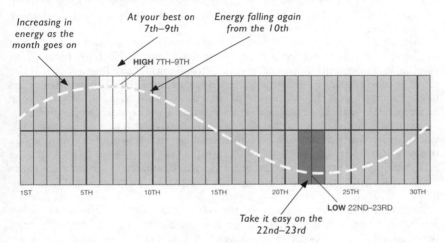

THE KEY DAYS

Some of the entries are in **bold**, which indicates the working of astrological cycles in your life. Look out for them each week as they are the best days to take action or make decisions. The daily text tells you which area of your life to focus on.

MERCURY RETROGRADE

The Mercury symbol (☿) indicates that Mercury is retrograde on that day. Since Mercury governs communication, the fact that it appears to be moving backwards when viewed from the Earth at this time should warn you that your communication skills are not likely to be at their best and you could expect some setbacks.

TAURUS: YOUR YEAR IN BRIEF

From the very start of the year you should be in a great frame of mind and quite anxious to get the very best out of any opportunity that comes your way. The winter months are not your favourite time of year. January and February should be fairly plain sailing however, and there is room for both changes at work and in your love life. You want to make a good impression on the whole world.

March and April should be reasonably smooth going but you might not be entirely satisfied with your progress at first. You are likely to be sluggish in your reactions and slower to respond to changing circumstances. All the same, it won't take you long to catch up with the field and then April offers new challenges and the possibility of achieving a longed-for objective. Keep an eye on the mail and answer all communications as quickly as possible.

It may seem as if the world doesn't understand you at first during May, but by June you will be back on course and anxious to get everything going the way you want. Throughout both months you have cause to look hard at relationships and you may not be quite as sure of yourself as would sometimes be the case. Still, you know how to work hard and how to get what you want in the end and that's what really counts.

July and August are likely to be the when you will travel the most, either for business or pleasure. If there are any problems at all during this time these are likely to be because you haven't checked details or because you are rushing again. Taureans who have been looking for a new relationship should focus their energies around now for maximum success.

The months of September and October can be quite peculiar in some ways. The changing circumstances between now and the end of the year might make you feel that you are on some sort of rollercoaster. However, this shouldn't really bother you too much because when one door closes for you, another will open straight away. Avoid any confusion by doing what you understand and by knowing what you intend to do at any given time.

November and December are likely to continue some of the favourable trends that have been around you for a while. You rush headlong towards Christmas and this might mean you lack the energy to get everything done. Nevertheless this should be a happy and generally successful time and one that brings you even closer to your heart's desire in a personal sense. By the very end of the year you show enterprise and be set on entering the New Year in the best possible style.

January 2018

YOUR MONTH AT A GLANCE

⊕ = Opportunities are around ⊖ = Be on the defensive ○ = Life is pretty ordinary

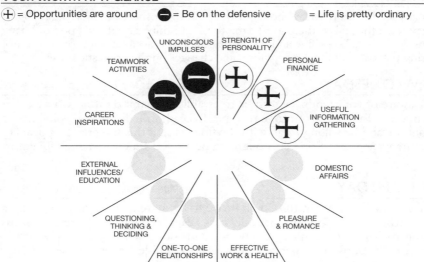

UNCONSCIOUS IMPULSES
STRENGTH OF PERSONALITY
TEAMWORK ACTIVITIES
PERSONAL FINANCE
CAREER INSPIRATIONS
USEFUL INFORMATION GATHERING
EXTERNAL INFLUENCES/ EDUCATION
DOMESTIC AFFAIRS
QUESTIONING, THINKING & DECIDING
PLEASURE & ROMANCE
ONE-TO-ONE RELATIONSHIPS
EFFECTIVE WORK & HEALTH

JANUARY HIGHS AND LOWS

Here I show you how the rhythms of the Moon will affect you this month. Like the tide, your energies and abilities will rise and fall with its pattern. When it is above the centre line, go for it, when it is below, you should be resting.

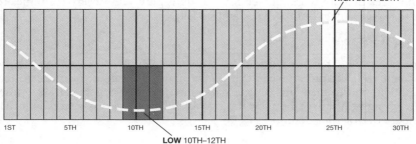

HIGH 25TH–26TH

1ST   5TH   10TH   15TH   20TH   25TH   30TH

LOW 10TH–12TH

1 MONDAY
Moon Age Day 14   Moon Sign Gemini

Stand by for a great start to the New Year! This first day should find you already in the mood to get new plans off the ground. Your capacity for work is very good at present, even if it takes quite a while for other people to get themselves into gear. The gentle side of your personality rules all romantic encounters helps you to support friends when they need it.

2 TUESDAY
Moon Age Day 15   Moon Sign Cancer

Focus on the future today and enjoy the positive prospects that surround you. It may seem that this is the perfect time to sit and think about the good old days, but while nostalgia is fine and has its place in our emotional suitcase, it may not bring practical benfits. Prepare for some changes on the domestic scene.

3 WEDNESDAY
Moon Age Day 16   Moon Sign Cancer

Be aware of your tendency to stick to established habit right now, a trait that can affect Taureans from time to time. Instead, look for new possibilities in your life and be willing to go with the flow, even if this sometimes appears to be the wrong direction. This ought to be a good time for change in almost every sense.

4 THURSDAY
Moon Age Day 17   Moon Sign Leo

In one way or another, this could prove to be quite a nostalgic period and a time when your mind automatically harks back to the past. There are lessons to learn here, but don't take any of them too much to heart. The future is an open book. Experience can be a good guide but it isn't everything, particularly when ingenuity is part of the package.

5 FRIDAY
Moon Age Day 18   Moon Sign Leo

Make up your mind to undertake something new and special today. It need not be expensive or even particularly difficult. The most important thing at this stage is that you set yourself challenges. There are a number of planetary influences that are working well for you right now, and variety continues to be the spice of life, both at work and socially.

6 SATURDAY
Moon Age Day 19   Moon Sign Virgo

There are many tests around at the moment when it comes to your ability to keep your life on an even keel. In the midst of change you need to feel confident and to maintain an external composure that others will recognise. There might, however, be a few times today when it's necessary to admit that you are out of your depth.

7 SUNDAY
Moon Age Day 20   Moon Sign Virgo

Good luck in your vicinity is apt to rub off on you and today's trends indicate that you stand a chance of enjoying a highly rewarding sort of day. Life really gets up to speed tomorrow but today would be good for short journeys or for shopping. A new level of comfort and security may be found in relationships, too.

8 MONDAY
Moon Age Day 21   Moon Sign Libra

Although you may be committed to getting things done at work, you will still be happy enough to spend social time with interesting and intelligent types. Your creative potential is as good as ever, perhaps even better than you would normally expect. You want to look good because that also makes you feel good. For sometimes showy Taurus, that's fine.

9 TUESDAY
Moon Age Day 22   Moon Sign Libra

Single Taureans especially may gain from present planetary positions, whilst those amongst you who are settled in established relationships should find them plain sailing. Your spirits are likely to be high and this is a day when you can sail through almost anything. Look out for romance and make the most of it as you charm everyone around you.

10 WEDNESDAY
Moon Age Day 23   Moon Sign Scorpio

Don't overestimate your abilities today. The monthly planetary lunar low has arrived and that can take a little of the wind out of your sails. Try to stick to what you know today and don't be quite so keen to be on the go from morning until night. Let others make the running, and be content to watch and wait for a while.

11 THURSDAY
Moon Age Day 24   Moon Sign Scorpio

You could be feeling quite lethargic and certainly not up to your recent standards. If you feel generally uninspired, take heart in the fact that this is just a very short interlude and in the knowledge that you will be in a much more positive frame of mind within a day or so, as the Moon moves out of your opposite sign.

12 FRIDAY
Moon Age Day 25   Moon Sign Scorpio

Remain as flexible as you can and be willing to admit that you don't have the monopoly on wisdom. If you are too adamant today you may feel something of a fool later. Being too preoccupied with a particular point of view is something that happens to the sign of Taurus now and again. Such is the case today but forewarned is forearmed.

13 SATURDAY
Moon Age Day 26   Moon Sign Sagittarius

There is great satisfaction to be gained from a job well done, even when the financial implications are not startling. Routines won't bother you right now – in fact you could welcome them. The pressure now seems to be on in a personal sense and you have to do everything you can to show what you are made of.

14 SUNDAY
Moon Age Day 27   Moon Sign Sagittarius

It's almost certain that both your enthusiasm and your physical strength are at a peak today. Good luck seems to be following you around, though of course it's really nothing of the sort because you are applying yourself positively to whatever you decide to do and make your own luck in this sense. Although you may have reservations, you may be inclined to speculate a little now.

15 MONDAY
Moon Age Day 28   Moon Sign Capricorn

You are now in one of the best periods for broadening your horizons and for coming to terms with the new starts that your chart suggests will soon be happening. Travel is positively highlighted, whether it is for business or pleasure. Be warned that comfort at home might be hard to come by if family members are in an organisational mood.

16 TUESDAY
Moon Age Day 0   Moon Sign Capricorn

It is unlikely that you will have to work very hard to win the support of important people today. In your domestic and family life, you might have to leave someone to their own devices, not an ideal state of affairs. In reality the situation is more positive than it looks because it prevents you from worrying about things you cannot control.

17 WEDNESDAY
Moon Age Day 1   Moon Sign Capricorn

Conversations you hear today can provide useful information, particularly with regard to professional matters. Although in some ways it is hard to keep up with everyone's expectations of you, by the end of the day you should discover that you have managed to achieve a great deal. Planetary trends are good today.

18 THURSDAY
Moon Age Day 2   Moon Sign Aquarius

Social matters bring a little light-hearted relief today, something you desperately need in order to avoid becoming too intense. When it comes to taking on new projects, the bigger the better seems to be your adage, though with plenty of co-operation and a high level of assistance you can get away with it.

19 FRIDAY
Moon Age Day 3   Moon Sign Aquarius

Whether you like it or not you are going to be on the go all day. That means pacing yourself and not taking on more than you have to. There can be great rewards for some of your present efforts but these are transitory and you run the risk of missing them altogether if you push on too soon with the next task. At least pause for breath.

20 SATURDAY
Moon Age Day 4   Moon Sign Pisces

Now you really want to get out into the world and show people what you are made of. Trends are more positive in a practical sense, whilst the level of your confidence is also growing. All of this means that you demonstrate your capabilities in everything you do. Friendship proves especially important by the evening.

21 SUNDAY
Moon Age Day 5   Moon Sign Pisces

A home-based Sunday appears to be on the cards. If this doesn't sound exciting enough for you, ring the changes by taking a short trip. More likely though, as present planetary trends suggest, you should be content with a simple day. You retain an excellent sense of fun and should be happy to demonstrate this to great effect.

22 MONDAY
Moon Age Day 6   Moon Sign Pisces

You ought to be feeling rather pleased with yourself at present, especially if you are at work today. Colleagues should be glad to put themselves out on your behalf and thinking on your feet is a piece of cake. Once work is out of the way, make a determined effort to spend a few hours with loved ones.

23 TUESDAY
Moon Age Day 7   Moon Sign Aries

Look out for a distinct advantage at work today, and don't be afraid to exploit it for all you are worth. There are people around who are in an excellent position to lend you a hand and you should not be too proud to make use of their services. When it comes to spending money, trends suggest that you should be just a little careful.

24 WEDNESDAY
Moon Age Day 8   Moon Sign Aries

There are times to argue, and periods when it is better to keep your counsel. The latter is the case right now, so don't become involved in any confrontations unless they are unavoidable. However, if you have no choice but to express your opinions, you should do so with all the clarity and conviction presently in your arsenal.

25 THURSDAY
Moon Age Day 9   Moon Sign Taurus

You should find that you have plenty of luck on your side as the working week grows older. The lunar high will find you full of beans and happy to make as much of your life as you can. Finances might be looking stronger and your capacity to make those around you happy knows no bounds. In almost every sense you should be feeling good.

26 FRIDAY
Moon Age Day 10   Moon Sign Taurus

With bounless confidence today you are on top form and, what's more, it seems that almost everyone you know wants to lend you a hand. The most important skill you possess today seems to be your ability to get your own way with almost everyone. When it comes to practical achievements you should be second to none now.

27 SATURDAY
Moon Age Day 11   Moon Sign Gemini

There are some strong supporting elements around in your chart now and you can make use of them. The fact is that one or two people think a great deal of you, and are willing to say so in public situations. Be willing to stand up for someone who is in trouble, even if you have to put yourself out significantly to do so.

28 SUNDAY
Moon Age Day 12   Moon Sign Gemini

Refuse to compromise on those occasions when you are certain that you are right. There are possible gains financially, plus you have a good eye for a bargain. For these reasons, you might decide that today would be good for shopping. If you overspend by just a pound or two – well, you can make up for it later.

29 MONDAY
Moon Age Day 13   Moon Sign Cancer

You probably crave a little peace and quiet today, though finding it may not be easy. Later in the day you could learn something that is definitely to your advantage, but you will need to take care that this does not lead you to unintentionally offend anyone else, particularly if all you are trying to do is to help.

30 TUESDAY
Moon Age Day 14   Moon Sign Cancer

There are times to be quiet, and times when you simply have to speak your mind. You can't lose at work today by being willing to express an opinion and doing so will probably mean that you get on in a general sense much better than anticipated. Rules and regulations could get on your nerves.

31 WEDNESDAY

Moon Age Day 15   Moon Sign Leo

Out there in the practical world you should be getting positive results. Money pressures are likely to ease, even if you don't feel exactly rich at present. Slowly but surely you are moving towards some important objectives and you maintain a positive attitude to life. Socially speaking you should avoid being a stick-in-the-mud and be open to invitations.

2018

YOUR MONTH AT A GLANCE

(+) = Opportunities are around ● = Be on the defensive ● = Life is pretty ordinary

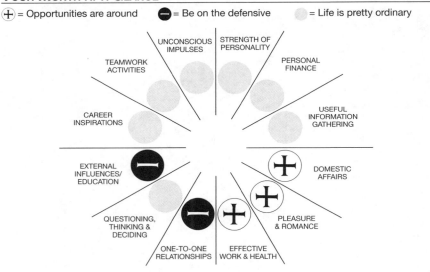

UNCONSCIOUS IMPULSES

STRENGTH OF PERSONALITY

TEAMWORK ACTIVITIES

PERSONAL FINANCE

CAREER INSPIRATIONS

USEFUL INFORMATION GATHERING

EXTERNAL INFLUENCES/ EDUCATION

DOMESTIC AFFAIRS

QUESTIONING, THINKING & DECIDING

PLEASURE & ROMANCE

ONE-TO-ONE RELATIONSHIPS

EFFECTIVE WORK & HEALTH

FEBRUARY HIGHS AND LOWS

Here I show you how the rhythms of the Moon will affect you this month. Like the tide, your energies and abilities will rise and fall with its pattern. When it is above the centre line, go for it, when it is below, you should be resting.

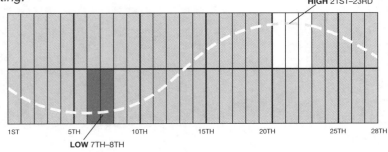

HIGH 21ST–23RD

1ST   5TH   10TH   15TH   20TH   25TH   28TH

LOW 7TH–8TH

1 THURSDAY
Moon Age Day 16   Moon Sign Leo

Young or young-at-heart Taureans can gain markedly from present planetary trends. Prepare for the fact that you might find it somewhat difficult to tell a friend exactly what you think. Keep up your efforts to gain materially but also take a look at romance, which appears potentially very good at present. With new associations developing, there is excitement about.

2 FRIDAY
Moon Age Day 17   Moon Sign Virgo

The chances are that you will be very motivated today, especially during the afternoon and evening. If you are feeling a surge of wanderlust, now is the time to exploit it by taking a journey. Don't be too quick to judge younger family members, no matter how they seem to be behaving. You might misunderstand their motivations.

3 SATURDAY
Moon Age Day 18   Moon Sign Virgo

You are frequently an independent type, though more so now than is generally the case. In social settings you shine much more than usual, but it is clear you prefer to be at the head of matters now. A situation that demands you relying heavily on others won't go down very well at all at a time when you want to make the running yourself.

4 SUNDAY
Moon Age Day 19   Moon Sign Libra

Specific planetary trends incline you to be more absent-minded than would usually be the case. Just as long as you review matters early in the day, and avoid forgetting anything important, you will proceed normally. Forgotten family gatherings are a distinct possiblilty at present. This might be a day for making lists.

5 MONDAY
Moon Age Day 20   Moon Sign Libra

You need to keep your eyes open because there are some helpful people and situations around. If you are presently engaged on a health kick of some sort, just remember that success comes through methodical application, not sudden change. Things that happen today could enhance your career prospects no end whether you work today or not.

6 TUESDAY
Moon Age Day 21   Moon Sign Libra

Some jobs prove to be so complicated you will want to go back the drawing board and start them again. Although others will disagree, you need to rely on your intuition in this regard. If you are in a position of some responsibility at work, do not allow your employees or workmates to question your decisions.

7 WEDNESDAY
Moon Age Day 22   Moon Sign Scorpio

The time is now right to slow down and to take a break. You might be feeling somewhat lacking in lustre and can really blame the position of the Moon for this state of affairs. Lunar lows are not usually too much of a problem to Taurus, which has a strong tendency to retreat into itself on occasion in any case. This is a day for thinking.

8 THURSDAY
Moon Age Day 23   Moon Sign Scorpio

One simple task at a time is the message today. Don't rush or push yourself into doing things that go against the grain and be willing to take hours out to think things through. The lunar low isn't going to have too much of a bearing on your life this time round, and especially not if you refuse to be hurried. This is a good day for dreaming.

9 FRIDAY
Moon Age Day 24   Moon Sign Sagittarius

You can't kiss winter goodbye for a while yet but may now be feeling less inclined to look back over the past months and instead more towards spring. You are gradually growing more confident in your own vision of the future. Remember that this won't be the case for everyone around you, though your persuasive skills could be useful here. Believe – and you can have almost anything now.

10 SATURDAY
Moon Age Day 25   Moon Sign Sagittarius

Your assertive nature is now quite clearly on display. This will come as a genuine surprise to some people and might be just what you need to wrong-foot the opposition. You won't take kindly to being told what to do, particularly in situations where you know you should be in the driving seat. Avoid being moody when little things go wrong.

11 SUNDAY
Moon Age Day 26   Moon Sign Sagittarius

This would be a good day for shopping or for spending some time in the company of lively and articulate friends. What you don't need at the moment is grumpy types. At work, situations should be beginning to improve, though it might be a little while before this becomes obvious. In the meantime, keep up your efforts.

12 MONDAY
Moon Age Day 27   Moon Sign Capricorn

Keep your eye on the ball, particularly at work and don't allow others to steal a march on you. Your generally steady approach to life is an advantage. Things may not be moving quite a fast as you would wish, and this could lead to some small frustrations as the day wears on. A few unforced errors on your part need to be avoided.

13 TUESDAY
Moon Age Day 28   Moon Sign Capricorn

Loved ones could be behaving in a strange and unpredictable manner, often leaving you guessing. For some relief you might turn in the direction of good friends, most of whom prove to be far less complicated at present. In the area of personal relationships, you will have to show extra special patience and tolerance.

14 WEDNESDAY
Moon Age Day 29   Moon Sign Aquarius

On the romantic front you may find that new offers are on the way this Valentine's Day – that is if you are interested in them. When it comes to professional matters, you can be quite successful at this time. With tremendous perception and an instinct with regard to what is likely to work for you, it's time to put your best foot forward.

15 THURSDAY
Moon Age Day 0   Moon Sign Aquarius

The need to be noticed is obvious and paramount for Taureans just at the moment. That's not too surprising because you are looking good and you know it. It isn't just your appearance that counts but also your attitude. Creative inspiration extends to changes you want to make in and around your home.

16 FRIDAY
Moon Age Day 1   Moon Sign Aquarius

Don't allow your home to become a battleground at the moment. Present planetary trends could find you at the centre of disputes, despite the fact that you are not the one who is creating them. Some tiredness is another consequence right now but you can counter this by involving yourself in interesting matters.

17 SATURDAY
Moon Age Day 2   Moon Sign Pisces

There ought now to be plenty of rewards to look forward to as far as your love life is concerned. Present planetary trends enhance the more charming side of your nature and this makes you a virtually essential companion to some people. Chatty and kind, the world looks favourably at you during this interlude.

18 SUNDAY
Moon Age Day 3   Moon Sign Pisces

Watch out for a few personal challenges at home as someone tries to usurp your position. This is something that you won't allow and you tend to react quite dynamically over such issues. Remember that the charm is still present and talk your way through issues that might sometimes spark off an argument.

19 MONDAY
Moon Age Day 4   Moon Sign Aries

It is possible that you will crave the security that comes from family relationships at this time. With just a little insecurity creeping in to your thoughts, you head back towards familiarity and routine. Staying out there in a world that looks threatening is for you like standing alone in the middle of a field during a thunder storm.

20 TUESDAY
Moon Age Day 5   Moon Sign Aries

You won't get everything you want today. The position of the Moon ahead of the lunar high stops you from pushing forward in quite the way you would wish, though it does allow you some time to think. The attitude of friends could be somewhat difficult to assess but if you have any doubt at all the best thing to do is to speak to them directly.

21 WEDNESDAY
Moon Age Day 6   Moon Sign Taurus

The lunar high this month places a positive focus on practical matters, which suits you down to the ground. Your sphere of influence is strong, both at work and at home. Changes you have been wanting to implement for some time now become entirely possible, especially in your current dynamic mindset.

22 THURSDAY
Moon Age Day 7   Moon Sign Taurus

Practically all everyday issues go according to plan and your progress should be generally smooth. You have what it takes to negotiate potential difficulties without even registering that there is a problem and should also enjoy a high degree of popularity. Best of all, Lady Luck is likely to pay you a visit so be prepared for her arrival.

23 FRIDAY
Moon Age Day 8   Moon Sign Taurus

Pressures are apt to arise in social relationships, even if most of them have nothing to do with you personally. If only for this reason you will probably choose to stick to those people you know the best, at least for today. This doesn't make you insular however, and you will be quite willing to show your friendly side.

24 SATURDAY
Moon Age Day 9   Moon Sign Gemini

Whilst you don't have absolute control over situations today, especially in a professional sense, you make the best of what you are personally able to achieve. This ensures that you get on generally well and you also have a silver-tongued eloquence that will surprise few, but charm everyone.

25 SUNDAY
Moon Age Day 10   Moon Sign Gemini

There are advantages about if you know where to look for them. Contrary to popular belief, financial matters are turning your way, whilst the social scene should look extremely interesting at this time. When it comes to impressing those around you, actions speak louder than words.

26 MONDAY
Moon Age Day 11   Moon Sign Cancer

This should prove to be an easier time than most for getting what you want professionally. Working Taureans should therefore pitch in fully and make the most of opportunities that come along. Some of the dross of life may have to be left alone, at least for the next day or two, but you will hardly mind that!

27 TUESDAY
Moon Age Day 12   Moon Sign Cancer

With an eye to the future, and good powers of communication at your disposal, this certainly won't be a stay-at-home-and-mope sort of day. It's true that you might have to make most of the running in all areas of life, but is unlikely to bother you at all. Give yourself credit for recent successes but keep soldiering on anyway.

28 WEDNESDAY
Moon Age Day 13   Moon Sign Leo

Trends suggest that you could be rather full of yourself today. That's fine just as long as you don't come across as being arrogant. Keep an open mind about ideas that others are putting forward. Even when you don't fully agree with a particular point of view you can contribute to changing it enough to make it workable.

March

2018

Your Month at a Glance

$\oplus$ = Opportunities are around $\ominus$ = Be on the defensive   ⚪ = Life is pretty ordinary

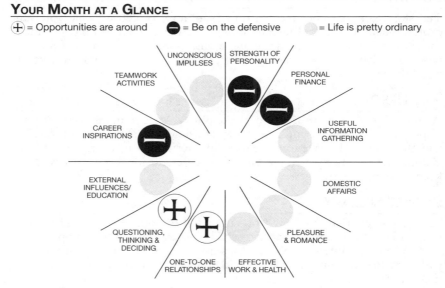

UNCONSCIOUS IMPULSES

STRENGTH OF PERSONALITY

TEAMWORK ACTIVITIES

PERSONAL FINANCE

CAREER INSPIRATIONS

USEFUL INFORMATION GATHERING

EXTERNAL INFLUENCES/ EDUCATION

DOMESTIC AFFAIRS

QUESTIONING, THINKING & DECIDING

PLEASURE & ROMANCE

ONE-TO-ONE RELATIONSHIPS

EFFECTIVE WORK & HEALTH

March Highs and Lows

Here I show you how the rhythms of the Moon will affect you this month. Like the tide, your energies and abilities will rise and fall with its pattern. When it is above the centre line, go for it, when it is below, you should be resting.

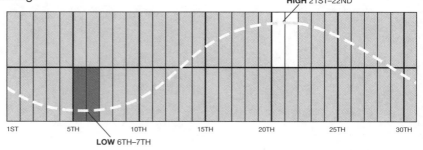

HIGH 21ST–22ND

1ST   5TH   10TH   15TH   20TH   25TH   30TH

LOW 6TH–7TH

58

1 THURSDAY
Moon Age Day 14   Moon Sign Leo

Trends suggest that group and co-operative ventures might be running less smoothly now than might have been the case over the last few days. With plenty to keep you occupied and probably little time to get everything done, some sort of plan is required. By the evening you should be feeling less harrassed.

2 FRIDAY
Moon Age Day 15   Moon Sign Virgo

Some jobs you have been expecting to be difficult might turn out less so than you thought. All in all, you could find people willing to help you and you might also discover new talents that you never knew you had. There is every reason why you should be enjoying social encounters at present and also finding new interests to fill your days.

3 SATURDAY
Moon Age Day 16   Moon Sign Virgo

Financial opportunities are there for the taking, and there is also the chance that you could receive some interesting romantic offers. Try not to make someone jealous by paying someone too much attention. Keep up a reasonable pace in life and don't be in the least surprised if you discover new responsibilities coming your way.

4 SUNDAY
Moon Age Day 17   Moon Sign Libra

Your creative potential seems to be especially good at the moment so you might decide this would be as good a time as any to make changes in and around your home. Away from home, there are plenty of interesting things going on and you will want to be involved in as many of them as possible. Take time to listen to loved ones in the evening.

5 MONDAY
Moon Age Day 18   Moon Sign Libra

Some special care is now required in certain matters. Things at work could go slightly off course and it is very important for you to keep your eye on the ball at present. Not many people will be in a position to get the better of you, so if there are any problems they could be self-created. Romantically speaking, you seem to be on the up.

6 TUESDAY
Moon Age Day 19   Moon Sign Scorpio

This would be a good time to enjoy a little peace and quiet. If possible, get away from the cut and thrust of everyday life and simply opt to please yourself. In a day or two the picture should have changed markedly, but for now you need to think things through and to listen to the small voice inside your head.

7 WEDNESDAY
Moon Age Day 20   Moon Sign Scorpio

Don't mishandle issues between yourself and someone who is important in your life. Use a little diplomacy and listen carefully to what is being said. On the financial front, it is possible that you are about to make an important decision but if you have already made up your mind, don't waver or delay. Make sure it is the right decision for you, though.

8 THURSDAY
Moon Age Day 21   Moon Sign Sagittarius

Take everything at face value and certainly don't doubt your own capabilities. Your concern for the underdog is high right now and this is a sure sign that your empathetic qualities are coming to the fore. You have the chance to make this a socially uplifting day, with much to set it apart and also the chance to get ahead in the career stakes.

9 FRIDAY
Moon Age Day 22   Moon Sign Sagittarius

Your confidence remains generally high, though there are people around who would change that situation if they could. Watch out for someone who wants to throw a spanner in the works. Mundane and domestic matters can be trying, which is why you are looking for diversity at this stage of the week and probably not sticking too close to home.

10 SATURDAY
Moon Age Day 23   Moon Sign Sagittarius

If you have been expecting a great deal of peace and quiet this weekend, you will probably be sorely disappointed. That doesn't mean there is anything negative about today. On the contrary, there is a great deal of enjoyment in store. The only proviso is that you have to let go in order to find and appreciate it.

11 SUNDAY
Moon Age Day 24   Moon Sign Capricorn

Despite your own efforts, it is others who conspire to make this Sunday potentially special, though you will need to look in the right direction in order to see it, particularly in matters of the heart. Someone from the past could pay a return visit to your life. This interlude promises to be interesting, and perhaps also surprising.

12 MONDAY
Moon Age Day 25   Moon Sign Capricorn

Travel and intellectual matters of all sorts are of particular interest to you during the first part of this week, at a time when you won't take at all kindly to being stuck in the same place. If you can't get away right now, don't despair. Your mind is working overtime and you ought to be able to work out a strategy to get a break soon.

13 TUESDAY
Moon Age Day 26   Moon Sign Aquarius

Practical issues and general run-of-the-mill situations are likely to take up much of your time today. Although you are likely to get plenty done, this probably could not be considered a particularly successful day. Your creative potential is especially good now and needs to be utilised in some way – and this could also lift your spirits.

14 WEDNESDAY
Moon Age Day 27   Moon Sign Aquarius

This is a particularly good day to be around the people you care for the most. Although you have been a distinctly social person on quite a few occasions this month, in the main you are happiest when you understand your surroundings and the people within it. All the same, one or two friends prove to be positively inspirational.

15 THURSDAY
Moon Age Day 28   Moon Sign Aquarius

It would be a good idea to vary your routines as much as possible right now and avoid too many strict plans. If you remain flexible, all sorts of possibilities will find their way to your door. People you haven't seen for some time could be making an appearance in your life soon. Look out for a quieter spell to come.

16 FRIDAY
Moon Age Day 29   Moon Sign Pisces

You might expect only moderate progress today. Unfortunately, you might feel that there are those about who appear to have a vested interest in preventing you from getting ahead. In reality this is almost certainly not the case, but if it is possible for you to get hold of the wrong end of the stick, this is a day when you could do so.

17 SATURDAY
Moon Age Day 0   Moon Sign Pisces

Be prepared to call in a few favours today because it is quite obvious that almost everyone is on your side. This is a weekend to remember, or at least it will be if you only put in a modicum of effort. General good luck aids almost any enterprise you choose and relationships should be the cause of much happiness. Try to be positive all day.

18 SUNDAY
Moon Age Day 1   Moon Sign Aries

Oh what a great day this can be in terms of love and romance. If there is someone out there you are anxious to get into a passionate embrace, this is the day to do it. Those Taureans who are in established relationships can also benefit from the present trends and you can afford to be very up-front in terms of wishes.

19 MONDAY
Moon Age Day 2   Moon Sign Aries

Your efforts to keep life on an even keel could be somewhat scuppered by the foolish actions of others today. Ignore this if you can and opt for a positive day, with plenty of social contact and a continued determination to break through barriers. Perhaps this is not a good time to listen to too much bad news.

20 TUESDAY
Moon Age Day 3   Moon Sign Aries

Intimate twosomes are characterised by a sense of harmony and good trends all round regarding love. On a practical level, life should feel secure and content, a good platform from which you can launch yourself confidently into new projects. Be bold in your assertions and don't allow anyone to deter you.

21 WEDNESDAY
Moon Age Day 4   Moon Sign Taurus

You can make today quite special. Acting on impulse is part of what the lunar high inspires you to do. Under most circumstances, you simply go for what you want and manage to obtain it. It looks as though you are likely to be dominant, though not in a way that is likely to upset anyone else in your vicinity.

22 THURSDAY
Moon Age Day 5   Moon Sign Taurus

The lunar high strengthens today, bringing a better sense of balance to your personality and making it easy for you to get along with just about anyone. Undertaking tasks you don't like the look of won't please you much, but there are times during the day when you are able to really let your hair down. This should be the highpoint of the month.

23 FRIDAY ☿
Moon Age Day 6   Moon Sign Gemini

Finding yourself in the right place at the right time to move onward and upward, you can once again show your true colours to the world at large. Although you may not get very much done in a practical sense today, it is possible to plan ahead and persuade people to help you with specific objectives.

24 SATURDAY ☿
Moon Age Day 7   Moon Sign Gemini

You have the chance today to broaden your personal horizons and to get on board with issues that might have puzzled you previously. Your friendship bonds are strong, and people who have not played an important part in your life up to now may also begin to become more significant to you. Look out for some unexpected financial gains as well.

25 SUNDAY ☿ *Moon Age Day 8   Moon Sign Cancer*

You can't avoid the feeling that this is an 'off with the old and on with the new' time in your life generally. That's fine, but don't go too far just because you are on a roll. It is just possible that you could abandon traditional ways of thinking and acting that are not at all redundant in favour of ones that don't serve you as well.

26 MONDAY ☿ *Moon Age Day 9   Moon Sign Cancer*

Where emotional ties are concerned, take a little more care than usual. It is easy for others to misunderstand what you are saying and to come to the wrong conclusions as a result. There are gains to be made through inventiveness and by being in the right place at the right time.

27 TUESDAY ☿ *Moon Age Day 10   Moon Sign Leo*

You can make this an extremely entertaining and positive sort of Tuesday. Picking from what seems like a whole variety of different possibilities, you tend to favour social projects above professional ones right now. Personal relationships ought to be working out especially well. Make this evening a time to remember.

28 WEDNESDAY ☿ *Moon Age Day 11   Moon Sign Leo*

The desire for fresh experiences is strong in you. Seeking out change and doing what you can to stimulate action, you will be able to embark on some interesting new adventures. Trends suggest that you cash increases, perhaps as a result of specific actions you have taken in the recent past. Enjoy yourself, but keep a sensible head on at all times.

29 THURSDAY ☿ *Moon Age Day 12   Moon Sign Virgo*

The planets today put you streets ahead of others: at work, or in any competitive endeavour. Don't fight shy of letting people know what you think. It's true that you are rather outspoken at the moment, but much of what you have to say makes a great deal of sense. Keep a sense of proportion regarding spending, even if you continue to enjoy some extra cash, and you will thank yourself for it.

30 FRIDAY ☿ *Moon Age Day 13   Moon Sign Virgo*

Your potential to making smooth and steady progress is strong. At work you should be able to address most matters well and will be unlikely to back down over issues you see as being important. Your personal life is likely to be settled, with some enjoyable romantic interludes permeating a generally sedate period.

31 SATURDAY ☿   *Moon Age Day 14   Moon Sign Libra*

Doing your own thing is the way forward now, rather than toeing a party line in any situation. You can be very stubborn when you feel you are being browbeaten and this is certainly no time to follow pointless instructions. Those who understand you the best will not be particularly surprised by your attitude.

2018

YOUR MONTH AT A GLANCE

$\oplus$ = Opportunities are around ⊖ = Be on the defensive ⬤ = Life is pretty ordinary

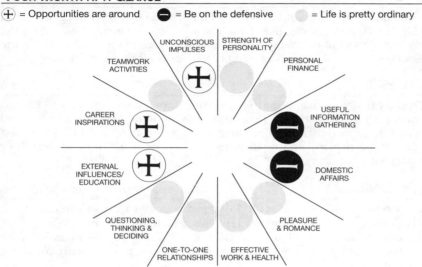

UNCONSCIOUS IMPULSES

STRENGTH OF PERSONALITY

TEAMWORK ACTIVITIES

PERSONAL FINANCE

CAREER INSPIRATIONS

USEFUL INFORMATION GATHERING

EXTERNAL INFLUENCES/ EDUCATION

DOMESTIC AFFAIRS

QUESTIONING, THINKING & DECIDING

PLEASURE & ROMANCE

ONE-TO-ONE RELATIONSHIPS

EFFECTIVE WORK & HEALTH

APRIL HIGHS AND LOWS

Here I show you how the rhythms of the Moon will affect you this month. Like the tide, your energies and abilities will rise and fall with its pattern. When it is above the centre line, go for it, when it is below, you should be resting.

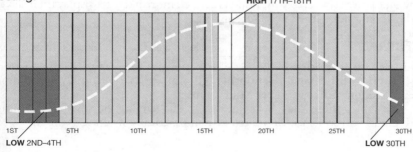

HIGH 17TH–18TH

1ST 5TH 10TH 15TH 20TH 25TH 30TH

LOW 2ND–4TH

LOW 30TH

1 SUNDAY ☿ *Moon Age Day 15   Moon Sign Libra*

If you know what you are talking about in any given situation, now is the time to speak out, even though it can take some courage to do so. Love life and romantic matters are continuing to show a distinct improvement. In a more practical sense, this is no time to be hiding your light under a bushel. Get out there and start speaking.

2 MONDAY ☿ *Moon Age Day 16   Moon Sign Scorpio*

It is no doubt true that you have to work quite hard now to get the good things of life but, being a Taurus, that doesn't worry you too much. Look out for the help and support of friends, some of whom have a good idea or two that in the fullness of time could make you significantly better off than you are now.

3 TUESDAY ☿ *Moon Age Day 17   Moon Sign Scorpio*

It is likely that your finances are looking quite good today, even if you have to stretch cash somewhat. Don't spend lavishly on items you don't really need and do be prepared to keep an open mind about bargains. Friends are on your side, particularly in little disputes that arise at work and you show how sensible you can be.

4 WEDNESDAY ☿ *Moon Age Day 18   Moon Sign Scorpio*

Few people would want to stand in your way at this time so you can afford to back your hunches, probably to the hilt. The middle of this working week ought to be an excellent time to take the odd chance and to stamp your own particular brand of authority on your life. Get to grips with any slight problem at home.

5 THURSDAY ☿ *Moon Age Day 19   Moon Sign Sagittarius*

With a ready wit and an ability to turn heads, you move more progressively towards your objectives now. There are hints that romance could be on the cards, particularly if you make some extra effort.
The quick-fire aspects of your mind are much more likely to display themselves today than at any time in the recent past.

6 FRIDAY ☿ *Moon Age Day 20   Moon Sign Sagittarius*

You need to give friends the benefit of the doubt, particularly in matters associated with personal relationships. If you are asked to offer an opinion that's fine, but otherwise keep your counsel.
All the same, there may be some really challenging personalities around today, and you seem to trip up over them practically wherever you go.

7 SATURDAY ☿ *Moon Age Day 21   Moon Sign Capricorn*

Your affable nature is on display this weekend. As a result, you should enjoy great popularity, especially when in the company of people you think a great deal about. Don't be in the least surprised if you find yourself being chatted up at some stage today. The social and friendship possibilities of the day are legion.

8 SUNDAY ☿ *Moon Age Day 22   Moon Sign Capricorn*

It would definitely be best to avoid getting into an argument today. Not only would be it completely unnecessary, but trends indicate that you don't stand much chance of winning it either! Far better to accept that you don't actually have to agree with everyone, and neither do you have to deliberately disagree. Keep your own counsel.

9 MONDAY ☿ *Moon Age Day 23   Moon Sign Capricorn*

Today is a period when you can't afford to accept second best in any situation. Your plans should receive plenty of support and you should enjoy a great deal of personal popularity. Especially in a social sense you should make the most of this. There are times to take a back seat and moments in your life when it's great to push to the head of the queue.

10 TUESDAY ☿ *Moon Age Day 24   Moon Sign Aquarius*

For today at least it might be better to accept something you cannot alter and get on with something different instead. There gains to be made financially, although probably not through gambling or any form of speculation. It is possible that someone is bugging you right now and, for a while at least, it looks like there's little you can do about it.

11 WEDNESDAY ☿ *Moon Age Day 25   Moon Sign Aquarius*

Get up and about and get a move on promptly today, avoiding the slightly lethargic tendencies to which Taurus sometimes succumbs. Give yourself a pat on the back for something you have recently achieved but don't become complacent. In most situations, there is still a long way to go and you may not have wrung the best out of professional possibilities.

12 THURSDAY ☿ *Moon Age Day 26   Moon Sign Pisces*

Keep an open mind about friends who call on your support. Though you might think one or two of them have been foolish, you can still be prevailed upon to help them out. You seem to be working well but you need to be aware that not everyone is doing what they can to be of assistance and a little prodding may be necessary.

13 FRIDAY ☿   *Moon Age Day 27   Moon Sign Pisces*

If you don't get everything you want today, it certainly isn't through a lack of application. In a positive and assertive mood, you have what it takes to make most situations your own and may be able to greatly influence the way other people are thinking. Continue to turn on the charm in the way you are doing at the moment and the world will be your oyster.

14 SATURDAY ☿   *Moon Age Day 28   Moon Sign Pisces*

It's time to get on and do things. There is plenty of support about if you are willing to go out and find it, but a few Taureans will now be insistent about going it alone. Don't be dissuaded from your personal desires or put off by obstacles. You have one of the most persistent and even stubborn natures in the whole zodiac and you can use this to your best advantage.

15 SUNDAY   *Moon Age Day 29   Moon Sign Aries*

Outdoor pursuits may hold a particular appeal for you today. The year is moving on, and with the lighter nights comes the feeling that you need some fresh air. Whatever you decide to do, take along someone you really like. The general routines of home life can wait for a couple of days while you amuse yourself.

16 MONDAY   *Moon Age Day 0   Moon Sign Aries*

It is likely that today could see specific financial or professional gains and would be an ideal time to start new projects, particularly at work. When the responsibilities are out of the way, you should think about having fun. Expect a mix and match sort of day, with periods of high activity and other times when you can relax.

17 TUESDAY   *Moon Age Day 1   Moon Sign Taurus*

Your creative potential is especially good and this would be an ideal time to put into action changes at home that have been on your mind. Today you are far more at ease in social situations and instead of mixing with people you find intimidating you choose to spend time with those with whom you are comfortable.

18 WEDNESDAY   *Moon Age Day 2   Moon Sign Taurus*

The lunar high is well underway making this a great day to make progress. The spotlight is on plans for special projects that are very close to your heart. Something you have been thinking about for a while may now become a reality, but this clearly has financial implications. You don't really look for security today but instead will be in the market for excitement.

19 THURSDAY
Moon Age Day 3   Moon Sign Gemini

Test your versatility by trying out new skills today. Yours is a zodiac sign that is often accused of being too fixed and inclined to follow rigid codes. So often this isn't the case at all. Now is the time when you can bend with the wind and make more out of life for yourself as a result. Progress is positive now.

20 FRIDAY
Moon Age Day 4   Moon Sign Gemini

The inner workings of your mind are revealed at the end of this working week as your natural spirituality comes to the fore. It is possible for you to be of great use to others, particularly those who are having a hard time at present. A quiet and compassionate approach to certain individuals may be required.

21 SATURDAY
Moon Age Day 5   Moon Sign Cancer

Look on this as being a problem-solving day. Your Taurean common sense is fully in place, as is a strong and trustworthy intuition. Subjecting things to the light or reason is not a problem and you also have a good ability to cut through red tape now, in order to get to the heart of what really matters.

22 SUNDAY
Moon Age Day 6   Moon Sign Cancer

Things seem to go so much better in pairs right now. In relationships you are relying more on your partner, or perhaps a trusted family member. Meanwhile, if you are at work today, you can trust a colleague to come up with the goods when it matters most. Maintain your sense of proportion – but don't let this override your intuition.

23 MONDAY
Moon Age Day 7   Moon Sign Leo

Look for wide open spaces now and realise that the year is moving on rapidly. Being stuck indoors all the time won't appeal to you at all and a breath of fresh air would clearly do you the world of good. When it comes to letting others know exactly how you feel, you should be second to none right now.

24 TUESDAY
Moon Age Day 8   Moon Sign Leo

There are a few possible gains to be made today, some of which come as a surprise. This means you have to be ready for almost anything. Your powers of communication are good at present and you can really make an impression when it counts the most. Don't be too quick to judge the wisdom of friends.

25 WEDNESDAY
Moon Age Day 9   Moon Sign Virgo

Some delays in favoured projects are inevitable now, which is why you may have to exercise a little patience, particularly during the middle of this week. Don't rush into anything, but use that capable Taurus brain and think things through carefully. A little preparation is worthwhile in any job you undertake today.

26 THURSDAY
Moon Age Day 10   Moon Sign Virgo

Your confidence grows gradually, but it certainly isn't at a height today. You may decide that the time is right to do some planning and to look ahead of yourself in practical issues. This is not really a day for taking risks, though this state of affairs is likely to change quite soon. Make the most of the evening.

27 FRIDAY
Moon Age Day 11   Moon Sign Virgo

As the working week draws to a close, there could well be a few tasks that have been left undone. You need to deal with these if you can, and to clear the decks for further action after the weekend. It is also important to make sure you won't have to worry about practical or professional issues over the weekend.

28 SATURDAY
Moon Age Day 12   Moon Sign Libra

The practical side of your nature is much in evidence, but unless you are really sure about what you are doing, you should still defer action until later. This Saturday is best for planning, and for observing the way others do things. You need these periods of calm and quiet in order to deal with the busier times that crop up regularly this year.

29 SUNDAY
Moon Age Day 13   Moon Sign Libra

Trends move on and today's message is now 'Don't put off until tomorrow something you can perfectly well do today'! Time seems to stretch like elastic, allowing you to get plenty done, and yet still leaving hours to spend in social pursuits, or with your partner. Taureans who are not romantically attached should keep their eyes open now.

30 MONDAY
Moon Age Day 14   Moon Sign Scorpio

Although your energy levels are not at an all-time high, thanks to the lunar low, you manage to get done those things that are necessary. You should find more get-up-and-go later in the day, when you will be occupied with matters that genuinely interest you. Keep an open mind about a romantic offer and certainly don't turn it down out of hand.

May

2018

Your Month at a Glance

⊕ = Opportunities are around ⊖ = Be on the defensive ○ = Life is pretty ordinary

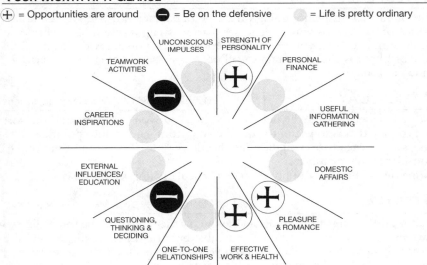

STRENGTH OF PERSONALITY
UNCONSCIOUS IMPULSES
TEAMWORK ACTIVITIES
PERSONAL FINANCE
CAREER INSPIRATIONS
USEFUL INFORMATION GATHERING
EXTERNAL INFLUENCES/ EDUCATION
DOMESTIC AFFAIRS
QUESTIONING, THINKING & DECIDING
PLEASURE & ROMANCE
ONE-TO-ONE RELATIONSHIPS
EFFECTIVE WORK & HEALTH

May Highs and Lows

Here I show you how the rhythms of the Moon will affect you this month. Like the tide, your energies and abilities will rise and fall with its pattern. When it is above the centre line, go for it, when it is below, you should be resting.

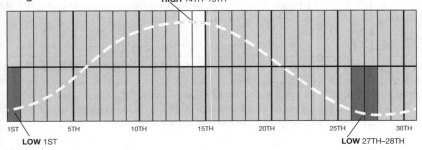

HIGH 14TH–15TH

1ST 5TH 10TH 15TH 20TH 25TH 30TH

LOW 1ST

LOW 27TH–28TH

1 TUESDAY
Moon Age Day 15   Moon Sign Scorpio

There might be periods of relative silence today but if so they tend to be chosen, rather than thrust upon you. Consideration for others is often high amongst your priorities and there is no reason to believe that today is any different. Avoid disappointments by not allowing yourself to get into positions that could prove awkward.

2 WEDNESDAY
Moon Age Day 16   Moon Sign Sagittarius

Although there is plenty going on in the outside world, you are taking less notice of it. Perhaps you want to set matters straight in a family sense or it could simply be that you realise how comfortable you are with life at home. The emphasis is almost certain to fall on personal and domestic concerns for much of today.

3 THURSDAY
Moon Age Day 17   Moon Sign Sagittarius

Not all planets are equally helpful now but you won't stop making the sort of progress that is so useful to you. Avoid putting energy into pointless tasks and settle instead for a slightly less hectic regime. Take some time out to consider family members.
Some quick thinking can prove to be particularly important today.

4 FRIDAY
Moon Age Day 18   Moon Sign Sagittarius

Put in a little extra effort on behalf of your partner and don't be too willing to cave in on a certain professional issue, just because others think you should. Everyday demands are likely to keep you pretty much on the go today and there is a good deal happening in life to interest you.

5 SATURDAY
Moon Age Day 19   Moon Sign Capricorn

Since you may not be at work today, do something really different and make sure you have allies who can make the day really enjoyable. Your general level of confidence isn't as high as it might appear, but you won't give any indication of this to others. Your sense of adventure grows and grows as the day wears on.

6 SUNDAY
Moon Age Day 20   Moon Sign Capricorn

Being an earth sign, Taurus can sometimes exhibit a strong stubborn streak and at such times will only do what it wishes. How true this is today. Despite this you can summon up a more flexible approach – that is if you really wish to do so. In all probability though, you will be quite content to show the more intransigent side of your nature until bedtime.

7 MONDAY
Moon Age Day 21   Moon Sign Aquarius

There is no need to argue your point today, simply because almost everyone automatically takes your side. Even people who have proved to be rather awkward in the past will be doing you some favours right now. On a few occasions today you could discover that circumstances are favouring you, even when things may not look promising.

8 TUESDAY
Moon Age Day 22   Moon Sign Aquarius

There is now no shortage of opportunities for your fertile mind. Flexible, interested and very friendly, you should surge through the day. If not everything is turning out the way you wish, maybe you are simply not trying hard enough. You will take great pleasure in being on the move at the moment but could stagnate if you stay still too long.

9 WEDNESDAY
Moon Age Day 23   Moon Sign Aquarius

The chances are that you will be able to understand what friends are asking of you, even when they are virtually silent. There should be plenty to smile about at present, especially when it comes to family matters. Even in relationships with those you don't know very well you should discover points of contact that bring a warmth to these associations.

10 THURSDAY
Moon Age Day 24   Moon Sign Pisces

Some friends could be slightly difficult to deal with and an extra dose of patience is likely to be necessary before the day is over. On the positive side, you could be on the receiving end of some very interesting news. There are also gains to be made on a personal and a professional level, though you can't expect everything to go your way.

11 FRIDAY
Moon Age Day 25   Moon Sign Pisces

Avoid being too set in your attitude. With plenty of energy now being piled into getting what you want from life, you should avoid any sort of argument with those you are going to have to rely on later. In the main you are very easy-going at present and probably won't be the one who creates difficult situations. You also tend to be quite intuitive today.

12 SATURDAY
Moon Age Day 26   Moon Sign Aries

Things are now looking good. In social matters especially, the impact of your personality is extremely strong at present. Do what you can to make a favourable impression, particularly amongst people who you know are on your side. There are some revolutionary ideas about at present and you are not shy about promoting them.

13 SUNDAY
Moon Age Day 27   Moon Sign Aries

Review all situations carefully and also look out for a real bargain, because they should be appearing at the moment. Generally speaking, things are on the up.

You might even find some shortcuts to success today, which isn't all that common for Taurus, a zodiac sign that is used to working hard for most of what it gets.

14 MONDAY
Moon Age Day 28   Moon Sign Taurus

The lunar high brings one of the high points of May. In today's bigger undertakings, you should discover that good luck is on your side and things just seem to fall into place. Getting your own way in group situations should be especially easy and remains so for a few days. Conversationally speaking, you should be on top form.

15 TUESDAY
Moon Age Day 0   Moon Sign Taurus

Stand by for a really interesting sort of day, made all the better by your very positive attitude. The world is opening up for you now in a number of ways and you will be seeking new paths towards some of your most important long-term schemes. There could be quite significant gains to be made on the financial front.

16 WEDNESDAY
Moon Age Day 1   Moon Sign Gemini

You may have little time for life's pleasures today as obligations get in the way. Because you are going to be such a busy Taurean it might be good to look at offers of help that might be on the table at this time. In relationships you need to keep a sense of proportion and to avoid reacting harshly.

17 THURSDAY
Moon Age Day 2   Moon Sign Gemini

There is now a major sense of urgency about getting things going the way you wish. True there are people around who threaten to throw a spanner in the works, though that really isn't too much of a problem. Avoid confrontations of any sort, since disputes simply won't help situations now.

18 FRIDAY
Moon Age Day 3   Moon Sign Cancer

This is a better time than most for keeping your eyes open and for making the best of any new situation that comes your way. You could hear some particularly interesting news regarding recent efforts you have made. Your creative potential is especially good and you are likely to be proud of a particular accomplishment.

19 SATURDAY
Moon Age Day 4   Moon Sign Cancer

Leave all routines alone and go for gold whenever you can right now. This is a weekend of activity and you make great achievements and progress in anything today and yet should still be well placed to enjoy time with friends and partners later on. Remember that the more time you can apportion to your own schemes today, the better things will go.

20 SUNDAY
Moon Age Day 5   Moon Sign Leo

Renewed emphasis on the world beyond your own door should enliven Sunday somewhat, though quite a few of you will find yourselves in relaxation mode. In rare cases, Taureans will be happy to spend at least some time alone daydreaming. Make the most of it, things are changing tomorrow.

21 MONDAY
Moon Age Day 6   Moon Sign Leo

You should remain happily on the go throughout most of today. Some of the recent cares are blown away on a breeze of excitement that is wafting through your life at this time. Don't spend too many hours trying to sort out the lives of people who are making no effort whatsoever to help themselves.

22 TUESDAY
Moon Age Day 7   Moon Sign Leo

Financially speaking the trends are now quite good. At work there is less pressure and maybe even enough time to enjoy yourself. You won't shy away from confrontation if it comes your way but would be unlikely to start it. If any aspect of life is becoming too routine today the secret is to change it.

23 WEDNESDAY
Moon Age Day 8   Moon Sign Virgo

Take advantage of circumstances that are clearly working in your favour. Although there are some slight obstacles to be overcome, the horizon today does look a good deal clearer than might have been the case recently. Friends prove to be extremely helpful, at a time when it matters the most.

24 THURSDAY
Moon Age Day 9   Moon Sign Virgo

In social matters especially, the impact of your personality is extremely strong at present. Do what you can to make a favourable impression, particularly upon people who you know are on your side. There are some revolutionary ideas about at present and you are not shy about promoting them.

25 FRIDAY
Moon Age Day 10   Moon Sign Libra

Standard responses won't work too well with some people now and you might have to be rather ruthless if you want to get your message across. There is never a reason to be cruel, but when you know you are working towards someone's good you can afford to go to town a little. Take care not to spark off minor family upsets, though.

26 SATURDAY
Moon Age Day 11   Moon Sign Libra

You could find this to be a rather taxing time if you are at work, leading you to be grateful once the responsibility is out of the way and you can finally please yourself. Socially speaking, you are on top form, which may be one of the reasons you are less professionally inclined just at the moment.

27 SUNDAY
Moon Age Day 12   Moon Sign Scorpio

Life could take on a rather so-so quality today, unless you put in that extra bit of effort that can make all the difference. Don't be willing to accept second best, either from yourself or others. The urge to see new places is still around you and you might decide to make use of the first part of the week for travelling around.

28 MONDAY
Moon Age Day 13   Moon Sign Scorpio

You should slow life down today and avoid taking on things that you know from the very start are going to be awkward. Give yourself time to think and to come to conclusions that are based on a mixture of intuition and common sense. You may not be too lucky with money today, which can be a legacy of the lunar low.

29 TUESDAY
Moon Age Day 14   Moon Sign Sagittarius

Your personality begins to shine out and is most obvious in the way you are happy to talk to anyone, about almost any topic. So noisy are you at present that it will be difficult for others to get a word in edgeways. It is unlikely that anyone will object because you are so good to have around now.

30 WEDNESDAY
Moon Age Day 15   Moon Sign Sagittarius

The potential for attracting money is sluggish now and isn't anywhere near as good as it was only last week. Still, you can tell yourself that the most important things in life have no monetary value. This is the Taurean spiritual ideal, but it might not prevent you from wanting those new shoes!

31 THURSDAY
Moon Age Day 16   Moon Sign Sagittarius

There is likely to be a very competitive side to your nature today, so you won't be happy if situations mean that you have to give in to anyone. As long as you don't allow this to lead to arguments, all should be well. Woe betide anyone who gets in your way in sporting encounters or over issues that really matter at work.

June

2018

YOUR MONTH AT A GLANCE

⊕ = Opportunities are around ⊖ = Be on the defensive ⚪ = Life is pretty ordinary

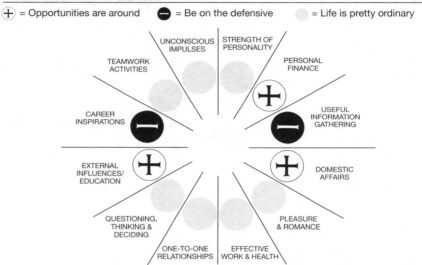

UNCONSCIOUS IMPULSES

STRENGTH OF PERSONALITY

TEAMWORK ACTIVITIES

PERSONAL FINANCE

CAREER INSPIRATIONS

USEFUL INFORMATION GATHERING

EXTERNAL INFLUENCES/ EDUCATION

DOMESTIC AFFAIRS

QUESTIONING, THINKING & DECIDING

PLEASURE & ROMANCE

ONE-TO-ONE RELATIONSHIPS

EFFECTIVE WORK & HEALTH

JUNE HIGHS AND LOWS

Here I show you how the rhythms of the Moon will affect you this month. Like the tide, your energies and abilities will rise and fall with its pattern. When it is above the centre line, go for it, when it is below, you should be resting.

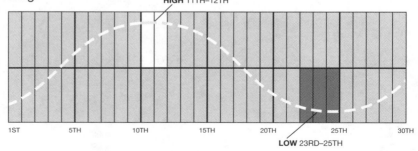

HIGH 11TH–12TH

1ST 5TH 10TH 15TH 20TH 25TH 30TH

LOW 23RD–25TH

1 FRIDAY
Moon Age Day 17   Moon Sign Capricorn

During this whole week you have been inclined to keep your eyes open but the arrival of Friday finds you less likely to be paying attention. This might be a pity because focus really counts at present. Don't miss out on anything important that is happening in or around your personal world and listen carefully to what is being said by friends or colleagues.

2 SATURDAY
Moon Age Day 18   Moon Sign Capricorn

The greater the range of interests you take on at the moment, the better you will enjoy life. You don't have to carry all your ideas into the future but taking them out of the drawer of your mind for a good examination at least allows you to decide what would be worth more effort in the longer-term. Friends may be demanding – but good fun.

3 SUNDAY
Moon Age Day 19   Moon Sign Aquarius

Don't be too quick to take offence if a friend says the wrong thing but ask for a fuller explanation. The planets incline you to be just a little quick off the mark around this time. Personal finance could be a slight cause for concern and it is probable that you are going to have to rein in your spending somewhat.

4 MONDAY
Moon Age Day 20   Moon Sign Aquarius

Rely on the support that your partner can offer and you could find a surprising turn in events happening at some stage during the first part of the day. Hard work is required and it will be necessary to see one or two jobs through to completion if you really want to profit now. Lay down a few plans for next week and look at your social schedule.

5 TUESDAY
Moon Age Day 21   Moon Sign Aquarius

Few aspects of life are working against your best interests right now. In some ways you find this to be an important turning point generally. Although changes look like being low-key, they are very significant in the end. If you want assistance for personal efforts, you will have the necessary cheek to ask for it today.

6 WEDNESDAY
Moon Age Day 22   Moon Sign Pisces

Care is necessary. There is always the chance that those around you could misconstrue what you are trying to say – and why. It's time to explain what you mean fully and to make the most of the support that comes from particularly good friends. Stay away from arguments altogether and opt for agreement whenever you possibly can.

7 THURSDAY *Moon Age Day 23   Moon Sign Pisces*

It's a fact that you have shown great kindness to others recently and some of these situations now pay dividends. Show family members how much you care about them and enjoy romantic possibilities. This is likely to be a generally good day and you can get your own way, mostly without seeming to try especially hard.

8 FRIDAY *Moon Age Day 24   Moon Sign Aries*

Your popularity is higher today than could have seemed to be the case yesterday and it appears that you know exactly what to say in order to get the right sort of reaction from others. Don't rush your fences when it comes to changes you want to make – but then being a Taurus you wouldn't! You could afford to trust your luck in some way this evening.

9 SATURDAY *Moon Age Day 25   Moon Sign Aries*

Help is there when you need it but for most of the time right now you are doing quite well enough under your own steam. The attitude of someone you know well appears somewhat unusual and so some gentle questioning may be necessary. In your career and professional matters generally, things ought to be going swimmingly.

10 SUNDAY *Moon Age Day 26   Moon Sign Aries*

If it seems that others are making mountains out of molehills maybe you should tell them, though as diplomatically as you know how. Hitting people in the face with situations is not going to help at all right now, so use all the tact you have at your disposal. This is especially true when dealing with professional superiors.

11 MONDAY *Moon Age Day 27   Moon Sign Taurus*

An unexpected favour could come your way today and general good luck seems to be almost everywhere you gaze. Progress is a definite possibility at the moment but more important still is the general popularity that attends your life and efforts today. At work and at home you seem to be everyone's number one during the lunar high.

12 TUESDAY *Moon Age Day 28   Moon Sign Taurus*

Tuesday continues the lunar high and a time during which you are bright, happy and likely to see the best in everything and everyone. You will have more energy and could sense that good luck is on your side. Plan now for some quite far-reaching practical changes you want to make as early as tomorrow and let your optimism shine out.

13 WEDNESDAY
Moon Age Day 0   Moon Sign Gemini

It appears that trends governing your love life are on the up and you can certainly turn heads wherever you go. Whether relationships are established ones or brand new, this is the time to get it on with the main person in your life. It is difficult to hide the sensual aspects of your earth-sign nature at this time, no matter how hard you might try. Taurus is likely to be sizzling.

14 THURSDAY
Moon Age Day 1   Moon Sign Gemini

The planets make it clear that nothing should be viewed too seriously around this time because there are plenty of jokers around – in fact you may be the most important of them. Get out and about if you can because some sort of journey would suit you down to the ground. Even a holiday at this time isn't out of the question.

15 FRIDAY
Moon Age Day 2   Moon Sign Cancer

Private matters are likely to occupy your mind a great deal today, though there is some sense of fulfilment when you manage to achieve objectives that have eluded you previously. It would be generally sensible to keep a low profile when in public situations and not to say too much unless you feel really confident.

16 SATURDAY
Moon Age Day 3   Moon Sign Cancer

Optimism is strong today and there isn't much at which you will fail when you also have confidence in your own abilities. People notice the new you and are anxious to back a winner. That increases your popularity and might mean a good deal of attention coming your way during the days ahead.

17 SUNDAY
Moon Age Day 4   Moon Sign Leo

Now that the summer weather is here you are likely to choose to divide your time between tasks that keep you indoors and those that offer a chance of some fresh air. The generally favourable trends are likely to continue for the moment, even if today lacks some of the excitement that has been obvious of late.

18 MONDAY
Moon Age Day 5   Moon Sign Leo

The general lift that comes with regard to career matters is certainly not going to pass you by today. In addition you ought to be feeling on top form mentally and physically. You have the ability to balance things well at present, which makes this an excellent time for taking any important decisions.

19 TUESDAY
Moon Age Day 6   Moon Sign Virgo

Keep your sights and effort on desires that are dear to your heart. At the same time spare an hour or two to support relatives or friends who are in need of your special support at this time. There are few limitations about just now, but that doesn't mean you are capable of doing everything at once – pace yourself.

20 WEDNESDAY
Moon Age Day 7   Moon Sign Virgo

The sort of contacts you are making at present are going to prove very important in the days and weeks ahead. Don't turn down the chance to meet anyone new and allay your natural suspicions regarding strangers. People are only unknown to you until the moment you bid them that first hello.

21 THURSDAY
Moon Age Day 8   Moon Sign Libra

A money matter requires a sensible approach and a good deal of your natural common sense today. When other people are refusing to see sense there isn't much you can do except to do your best to persuade them that you know what you are talking about. Your confidence is not lacking, as you are about to find out!

22 FRIDAY
Moon Age Day 9   Moon Sign Libra

Take every advantage to get ahead today, whilst at the same time realising just how much can come your way through simply having fun. Arguments should be strenuously avoided because they won't get you anywhere now. Use today to reassure particular relatives or your partner if they are feeling insecure in any way.

23 SATURDAY
Moon Age Day 10   Moon Sign Scorpio

Allow others to deal with some of the details of life, whilst you concentrate on taking your time and watching the flowers grow. Normally the lunar low arriving at the weekend might put something of a dampener on your life. Nothing could be further from the truth this time round, so enjoy the break.

24 SUNDAY
Moon Age Day 11   Moon Sign Scorpio

It would be best not to expect too much in the way of action today, as the Moon is still in your opposite zodiac sign. All the same, you should find it easy to ask for what you want, since few people would be likely to refuse you. Keep up your efforts to improve the quality of your relationships and to please people who are important to you. There is time enough for practical matters once the Moon has moved on.

25 MONDAY
Moon Age Day 12   Moon Sign Scorpio

The more time you can give to your own schemes today the better things will go, especially as the Moon leaves your opposite sign later in the day. Leave all routines alone and go for success whenever you can. As your activity levels increase, you can get through plenty of work and will have energy for your social life in the evening.

26 TUESDAY
Moon Age Day 13   Moon Sign Sagittarius

Friendships need that extra touch of effort to make them work properly. There is a strong chance that those around you are behaving in strange ways. This being the case you need to make the compromises. Don't allow your perceived sense of your own limitations to become known to others or you might just find they start to become true.

27 WEDNESDAY
Moon Age Day 14   Moon Sign Sagittarius

Now you can make your move, both at work and in personal situations. To the outside world you look successful and impressive, which means you are probably at the peak of your powers. Even if you don't feel entirely certain of yourself, it is the impression you give that means the most.

28 THURSDAY
Moon Age Day 15   Moon Sign Capricorn

Most matters can go your way today, with just a little effort on your part. If there are celebrations in the family or within your friendship circle, there's a good chance you will want to join in. You have a fairly carefree attitude to life at present and can certainly enjoy all that romance offers.

29 FRIDAY
Moon Age Day 16   Moon Sign Capricorn

Don't believe everything you hear today because the chances are that someone is deliberately trying to fool you. Subject everything to the same level of Taurean scrutiny and give some thought to testing one or two of your big ideas before you put them into practice.

30 SATURDAY
Moon Age Day 17   Moon Sign Capricorn

Your love life enjoys a definite boost given the planetary position at the start of the weekend. This may also be partly due to the fact that you have more time to concentrate on the needs of those around you, particularly your partner. Don't be too quick to volunteer for jobs around the home because they can mount up.

July

2018

YOUR MONTH AT A GLANCE

(+) = Opportunities are around ⊖ = Be on the defensive ⬤ = Life is pretty ordinary

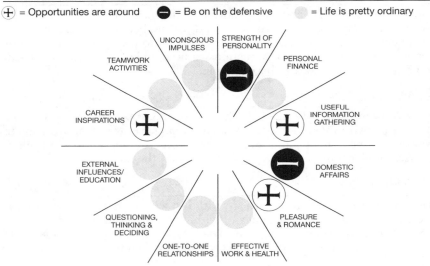

UNCONSCIOUS IMPULSES

STRENGTH OF PERSONALITY

TEAMWORK ACTIVITIES

PERSONAL FINANCE

CAREER INSPIRATIONS

USEFUL INFORMATION GATHERING

EXTERNAL INFLUENCES/ EDUCATION

DOMESTIC AFFAIRS

QUESTIONING, THINKING & DECIDING

PLEASURE & ROMANCE

ONE-TO-ONE RELATIONSHIPS

EFFECTIVE WORK & HEALTH

JULY HIGHS AND LOWS

Here I show you how the rhythms of the Moon will affect you this month. Like the tide, your energies and abilities will rise and fall with its pattern. When it is above the centre line, go for it, when it is below, you should be resting.

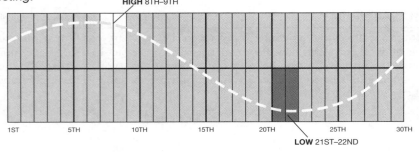

HIGH 8TH–9TH

1ST 5TH 10TH 15TH 20TH 25TH 30TH

LOW 21ST–22ND

1 SUNDAY
Moon Age Day 18   Moon Sign Aquarius

This looks like a sound day. You should be in a very good position to call the shots at the moment, not least of all because those closest to you, especially if you are at work, are more than happy to follow your lead. Avoid anxiety regarding issues you cannot influence and be willing to give a friend the benefit of the doubt.

2 MONDAY
Moon Age Day 19   Moon Sign Aquarius

It appears that the wheels of progress turn well, sometimes even despite the fact that you don't appear to be contributing too much. Financially it seems that you are now dealing with situations one at a time. Taurus is coming into its own, especially when making decisions proves to be particularly important.

3 TUESDAY
Moon Age Day 20   Moon Sign Pisces

A definite interest in what makes the world tick can set this Tuesday apart, though quite a few Taureans will find themselves switching into relaxation mode. There are many changes to come in the days ahead and directly conflicting interests to be dealt with. Get together with likeminded individuals later.

4 WEDNESDAY
Moon Age Day 21   Moon Sign Pisces

Now you have increased concentration and perception levels, which lifts the possibilities for the midweek no end. Although you can now get on very well in a practical sense, it is the social trends that count the most. A very unusual streak comes along and Taurus is now far more willing to look at long-shots and calculated risks.

5 THURSDAY
Moon Age Day 22   Moon Sign Pisces

Your confidence in your ability to do the right thing remains generally high and you won't be easily distracted from the task at hand. Although it might be easy to submit to pressure today, you are unlikely to do so. You would be well advised to abandon whatever isn't working and to concentrate instead on a few simple strategies.

6 FRIDAY
Moon Age Day 23   Moon Sign Aries

One-to-one relationships could seem to suffer a few setbacks today and, in fact, tomorrow also. The best way to deal with this situation is to mix more freely and with a number of different people. Don't allow yourself to be restricted by pointless red tape or by rules and regulations you simply do not understand.

7 SATURDAY
Moon Age Day 24   Moon Sign Aries

For today at least you might find yourself rather alone when it comes to pressing ahead in quite the way you would wish. This is a very temporary situation and not one that will trouble you all that much in any case. Your partner should be able to provide a sense of emotional security, which is what matters most at present.

8 SUNDAY
Moon Age Day 25   Moon Sign Taurus

Look out for a physical peak and a time during which it is very easy for you to overthrow previous obstacles and to get ahead famously. Not everyone is on your side at the moment but it really doesn't matter because you are a human whirlwind and know exactly how to get the best from any situation that you encounter.

9 MONDAY
Moon Age Day 26   Moon Sign Taurus

This should be a good day and one during which you have everything you need to make the best possible impression, not least of all on people who really count. There are gains to be made financially and also with regard to romance. Don't be too quick to make a judgement of your own past efforts. They are better than you think.

10 TUESDAY
Moon Age Day 27   Moon Sign Gemini

Look ahead and plan carefully, though you cannot afford to be too hesitant or you could miss opportunities of the moment. Some small disappointments concerning your romantic life could take the edge off an otherwise fairly positive period but this is only likely if you leave yourself open to such possibilities.

11 WEDNESDAY
Moon Age Day 28   Moon Sign Gemini

Thanks to present planetary trends your imagination is likely to be working overtime, which has good and bad repercussions. You can imagine all sorts of monsters but none of them has any substance whatsoever. If you feel the weight of certain worries, tackle them one at a time and with the help of people who are in the know.

12 THURSDAY
Moon Age Day 29   Moon Sign Cancer

It is your practical skills that always win out in the end, together with that famous Taurean common sense. Even if you are young in years it becomes obvious today that you are old in terms of wisdom. Trends assist you to become powerful in some situations now and people really do listen to what you have to say – which is a great deal more than sometimes happens.

13 FRIDAY
Moon Age Day 0   Moon Sign Cancer

There is great potential about but not if you remain in the same position all the time. A little excitement could be on the way, possibly as a result of the actions of a friend. You would also gain significantly from altering a business habit. Go for variety and a change of scene if you can today

14 SATURDAY
Moon Age Day 1   Moon Sign Leo

Your sense of personal security is as important now as it ever gets to be. If you were a medieval monarch, you would now be opening all your treasure chests and counting the gold pieces. As it is, you are likely to show a great tendency to make sure that all details are sorted and that your path ahead is unobstructed.

15 SUNDAY
Moon Age Day 2   Moon Sign Leo

Look out for interesting contacts. Some of these will be people you already know but your life is in such a state of flux there are bound to be new individuals around too. Acting on impulse seems attractive from a personal point of view and it is true that you are very disarming right now, so perhaps it is the best policy.

16 MONDAY
Moon Age Day 3   Moon Sign Virgo

Social matters tend to represent the most rewarding aspect of life at this time. That's not to suggest that you are failing to do what is necessary at work too. It ought to be possible to mix business with pleasure to a great extent and to offer the best of what Taurus can be to the world at large.

17 TUESDAY
Moon Age Day 4   Moon Sign Virgo

Social highlights today find you in good company and even more willing to have a go at things generally. If there isn't quite the level of zest around that was with you recently, you can at least rely on the fact that you will be feeling generally secure. This is a real must for Taurus.

18 WEDNESDAY
Moon Age Day 5   Moon Sign Libra

Good friends are worth spending more time with today. These are the people who are not afraid to tell you the way things are. Of course you don't always relish their words but you do know why they say the things they do. It is possible to achieve real closeness and warmth at any stage during this twenty-four hour period.

19 THURSDAY
Moon Age Day 6   Moon Sign Libra

Interests, especially creative ones, come thick and fast this Thursday. It's likely that you will be making the most of the summer too, so the ideal situation might be to do something constructive in the garden. Socially speaking you are quite able to mix with others but it isn't essential to do so right now.

20 FRIDAY
Moon Age Day 7   Moon Sign Libra

It is possible that some Taureans will feel overtaxed by work commitments at this stage of the month. If this is the case, and you have time owing to you, why not consider a day away from work? The break would clearly do you good and would offer you the hours you require to sit back and think.

21 SATURDAY
Moon Age Day 8   Moon Sign Scorpio

The lunar low has arrived and you don't really have what it takes to get ahead for today at least. All the same you can rely on the help and support that comes from some very important people in your life and will be basking in the joy that romance can bring. The trends in a day or two will be better but you are not likely to be overly unhappy at the moment.

22 SUNDAY
Moon Age Day 9   Moon Sign Scorpio

Let your partner or family members make major decisions, if indeed any have to be made today. For your part, you should be more than happy to take a break and to decide later how matters should be addressed. If you spend time at home and relax, you may not even notice that there are any constraints around you at all.

23 MONDAY
Moon Age Day 10   Moon Sign Sagittarius

A little soul-searching might be required. Review the recent past carefully and decide what needs to change in your life in order to make you feel more confident for the future. Don't spend all day on this task though. There are people and places waiting for you, and some interesting possibilities as a result.

24 TUESDAY
Moon Age Day 11   Moon Sign Sagittarius

This is a time of the month when you have it within yourself to talk almost anyone into doing what you want. With excellent powers of communication, a real zest for life and a great deal of joy to bestow on the world, stand by for one of the best potential days of the month. Of course what you make of it is up to you.

25 WEDNESDAY — *Moon Age Day 12   Moon Sign Capricorn*

Your love life tends to have its slight problems right now. For starters you are not so willing or able to see the other person's point of view. Extra flexibility is going to be required and you must do everything you can to examine points that are put to you before you react strongly against them. Failure to do this will certainly lead to trouble.

26 THURSDAY — *Moon Age Day 13   Moon Sign Capricorn*

It would be best to opt for some light relief today and this is something you should be thinking about. There are substantial gains to be made where friendship is concerned, and sociable associations with others could also lead to you discover ways to get ahead in a financial as well as a personal sense.

27 FRIDAY — *Moon Age Day 14   Moon Sign Capricorn*

A slight lack of confidence in your own ideas or abilities could get in the way of advancement at the moment. You need to be certain of your facts, as is always the case for Taurus. Do a little research and when this is completed, then you can decide what is the best course of action and follow it accordingly.

28 SATURDAY — *Moon Age Day 15   Moon Sign Aquarius*

A more socially helpful period is at hand, during which those around you are more willing than ever to put themselves out on your behalf. Don't be too quick to judge the actions or opinions of a friend, but remain flexible and even suggestible. Routines look likely to bore you today so avoid them if you can.

29 SUNDAY — *Moon Age Day 16   Moon Sign Aquarius*

This is a better time than most in which to keep your eyes and ears open for new chances of almost any sort. In a creative and artistic mood, you instinctively know what looks and feels right. Moving outside your usual social mainstream, you probably feel more alive than has been the case for some days. Enjoy the feeling this produces.

30 MONDAY — *Moon Age Day 17   Moon Sign Pisces*

Getting away from any sort of rat race appeals to you at the start of this new week. If has proved to be possible to have an extended weekend, this would suit you best of all. However, the fact that you might be somewhat withdrawn at the moment doesn't mean that you are failing to come up with some startling ideas.

31 TUESDAY
Moon Age Day 18   Moon Sign Pisces

Don't be afraid to consider specific changes to your life if you know in your heart that they are going to benefit you later. Not everything will go your way today but you should be enjoying the summer and making the most of every opportunity to find fresh fields and pastures new.

2018

Your Month at a Glance

⊕ = Opportunities are around   ⊖ = Be on the defensive   ⬤ = Life is pretty ordinary

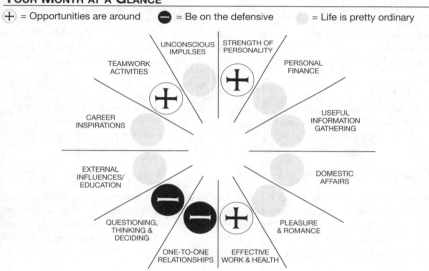

UNCONSCIOUS IMPULSES

STRENGTH OF PERSONALITY

TEAMWORK ACTIVITIES

PERSONAL FINANCE

CAREER INSPIRATIONS

USEFUL INFORMATION GATHERING

EXTERNAL INFLUENCES/ EDUCATION

DOMESTIC AFFAIRS

QUESTIONING, THINKING & DECIDING

PLEASURE & ROMANCE

ONE-TO-ONE RELATIONSHIPS

EFFECTIVE WORK & HEALTH

August Highs and Lows

Here I show you how the rhythms of the Moon will affect you this month. Like the tide, your energies and abilities will rise and fall with its pattern. When it is above the centre line, go for it, when it is below, you should be resting.

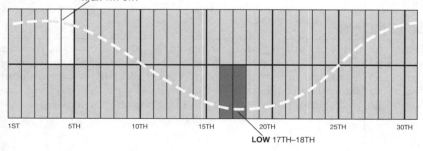

HIGH 4TH–5TH

1ST   5TH   10TH   15TH   20TH   25TH   30TH

LOW 17TH–18TH

1 WEDNESDAY ☿   *Moon Age Day 19   Moon Sign Pisces*

Finding time to do what pleases you personally will be quite difficult today but since you are probably on the go from morning until night this might not occur to you until later. There is certainly no doubting your loyalty at present, nor your commitment to people who have looked after you in the past.

2 THURSDAY ☿   *Moon Age Day 20   Moon Sign Aries*

Today you may enjoy some interesting romantic moments, or just possibly thoughts regarding a new friendship, together with a slightly more solid time on the financial front. What a good period this is for entertaining new ideas, specifically ones that are going to help you get ahead in a financial sense later.

3 FRIDAY ☿   *Moon Age Day 21   Moon Sign Aries*

For the moment it is better to judge by your own intuition, which is strong today. Some of your conclusions might be said to verge on the psychic because they are so accurate. Don't be taken in too easily by the tales others are telling. Many of these will be distorted, or downright wrong.

4 SATURDAY ☿   *Moon Age Day 22   Moon Sign Taurus*

Along comes a really good time as the Moon moves into your own zodiac sign of Taurus. Although the lunar high happening at the weekend doesn't offer too much scope in a professional sense, it certainly does have a bearing on your social and domestic life. Do what you can to enjoy yourself and relish situations to the full.

5 SUNDAY ☿   *Moon Age Day 23   Moon Sign Taurus*

This could be the high point of the month concerning travel and will see many Taureans packing their bags and jetting off somewhere or other. It doesn't really matter how near or far you go. The important thing is that you have worked hard of late and could do with a genuine change of pace.

6 MONDAY ☿   *Moon Age Day 24   Moon Sign Gemini*

Listen to family members, some of whom have an important message to impart. Things on the work front can become rather sluggish, so all the better if you are not over-committed professionally at the moment. Prevailing planetary influences could make life slightly less exciting than you might wish, though, with effort, you can pep it up somewhat.

7 TUESDAY   ☿   *Moon Age Day 25   Moon Sign Gemini*

Don't necessarily believe all you hear from others, even friends. People could be quite misinformed at the moment. This ought to be a fairly good time with regard to money. What you already have you tend to keep, whilst the possibility of making more is never far away and especially good for Taurus now.

8 WEDNESDAY   ☿   *Moon Age Day 26   Moon Sign Gemini*

Co-operation at work can be worth a great deal and leads to better prospects for all in the end. You could be called on to supervise something, which will bring kudos. Although you are well into a fairly busy schedule there ought to be time to please loved ones and to make a fuss of friends.

9 THURSDAY   ☿   *Moon Age Day 27   Moon Sign Cancer*

Not everyone in your environment will prove to be equally helpful today, so take care to turn in the right direction and then you can be sure of the sort of support you are looking for. Trends place a strong emphasis now on broadening your horizons and on making sure you are in the right place at the right time to get ahead.

10 FRIDAY   ☿   *Moon Age Day 28   Moon Sign Cancer*

The astrological circumstances today suggest you adopt whatever attitude suits you the best on a personal level. The escape you still want to make at present could be either outwards or inwards. Some Taureans are likely to be in an introspective mood towards the day and will be lost in their own dreams.

11 SATURDAY   ☿   *Moon Age Day 0   Moon Sign Leo*

The weekend ought to be bright, cheerful and full of exciting events. If it doesn't look as though things are going to turn out that way of their own accord, then do something about it! This is not a time to be a wallflower or to hang back in any way. Now you can afford to dispense with caution and take life by the scruff of the neck.

12 SUNDAY   ☿   *Moon Age Day 1   Moon Sign Leo*

Everything looks fairly good. Career issues should be quite fulfilling, even though so many of you won't actually be working on a Sunday. To make use of these trends, set some time aside to to plan for the working week, although don't give all of the day to this. People around you clearly wish to have fun and you will want to join in.

13 MONDAY ☿
Moon Age Day 2   Moon Sign Virgo

Look out for love knocking on your door and don't turn away from the chance to show what you can really do. Expect some upheavals at home with your family, although you will not be the one causing them. Put some ingenious ideas to the test and enlist the help of likeminded people whenever you can today.

14 TUESDAY ☿
Moon Age Day 3   Moon Sign Virgo

Take things steadily in a professional sense, but don't be afraid to paint the town red once work is out of the way. Any form of outdoor activity suits you down to the ground during this week. There is an indication that you could still be in the dark regarding information you have a long time for, and some patience may be required here.

15 WEDNESDAY ☿
Moon Age Day 4   Moon Sign Libra

A change of attitude might be necessary. Standard responses might not work too well with some people now and you might have to be rather ruthless if you want to get your message across. Take care not to take this too far, though, or people will deliberately switch off from your message. Avoid minor family upsets as much as possible.

16 THURSDAY ☿
Moon Age Day 5   Moon Sign Libra

It is paramount to make sure that others don't misconstrue what you are saying today. Find some space to be yourself and react as naturally as you can, while making sure that you explain yourself properly. It is worth double-checking your decisions before you put any really important plan into action.

17 FRIDAY ☿
Moon Age Day 6   Moon Sign Scorpio

Avoid pushing yourself too hard today. The monthly lunar low has arrived, but you should be far enough ahead in a general sense not to have to rush through it regardless. Take time out to look, to think and to plan. Personal attachments should be sound and capable of providing a warm glow when you need it the most.

18 SATURDAY ☿
Moon Age Day 7   Moon Sign Scorpio

Life may still not be looking particularly exciting and there are times today when it would definitely easier to do something yourself rather than trying to get someone else to do it. All the same, you need a rest so this would not be the best day of the month to push yourself too hard or to expect too much of your depleted forces.

19 SUNDAY
Moon Age Day 8   Moon Sign Sagittarius

The emphasis now seems to be on the domestic scene. Fight shy of concentrating only on this sphere of your life because you clearly need variety. The more stimuli that is coming in, the better is your ability to quantify people and situations. Taurus is super logical today, although take care that this does not bring problems of its own.

20 MONDAY
Moon Age Day 9   Moon Sign Sagittarius

At work you should now have more power at your fingertips and a better idea of how you should go about specific tasks. The more you get done today the better is your chance of enjoying some relaxation later in the week. There are good prospects for travel before next weekend but you will need to plan ahead to make the most of them.

21 TUESDAY
Moon Age Day 10   Moon Sign Sagittarius

You will now be happy taking an easy, freewheeling approach to life. True this isn't the Taurean way as a rule but you simply can't help your present desire to allow change to run you. It takes courage to follow such trends through to their natural conclusion without applying the brakes, but the effort could be worthwhile.

22 WEDNESDAY
Moon Age Day 11   Moon Sign Capricorn

A natural healing takes place in your life at this time. If there is a friendship, or even a deeper relationship, that has gone wrong in the past, now is the time to address it. You are in a particularly forgiving frame of mind and will almost certainly find other people willing to start afresh as well.

23 THURSDAY
Moon Age Day 12   Moon Sign Capricorn

Although your potential luck in a monetary sense is slightly less defined today, in terms of relationships things should still be buzzing. Your nervous system might be somewhat up and down at present but there isn't anything particularly unusual about that for your zodiac sign. Set some time aside to meditate at some stage today.

24 FRIDAY
Moon Age Day 13   Moon Sign Aquarius

With so much emphasis on personality and self, you can hardly fail to cause a raised eyebrow from one direction or another. Fortunately people are hardly likely to consider you either arrogant or vain at the moment. This ought to be the best of all possible days; that is if you are using your skills to the full.

25 SATURDAY
Moon Age Day 14   Moon Sign Aquarius

Hot August days probably put you in a romantic frame of mind. If you are looking for love, now is the time to keep your eyes open. More established relationships can also benefit from present trends, whilst acquaintances are less important and work is very far at the back of your mind this weekend.

26 SUNDAY
Moon Age Day 15   Moon Sign Aquarius

Look out for a slightly difficult day emotionally. You need to be absolutely sure that you understand what others are saying, particularly your partner. As long as you are willing to talk things through steadily, then all should be well. What you shouldn't do is fly off the handle without being fully in possession of all the facts.

27 MONDAY
Moon Age Day 16   Moon Sign Pisces

You now enjoy the company of a whole host of different sorts of people. Be willing to spend time with unusual types who have a very different view of life than the one you generally hold. Don't allow yourself to become involved in family rows. You won't be starting them and haven't a great deal to contribute.

28 TUESDAY
Moon Age Day 17   Moon Sign Pisces

Avoid ill-conceived ideas, most of which probably come from someone else in any case. Don't commit yourself to anything until you have looked closely at the details and are certain of your options. It might be best to stay right away from business of any sort if you can today because pleasure is now more rewarding.

29 WEDNESDAY
Moon Age Day 18   Moon Sign Aries

There are certain emotional pressures that you will have to work against today. Don't be too quick to push your point of view forward, particularly when you are talking to your partner or loved ones. Your confidence remains generally high, but you can't be certain of bringing everyone on side now.

30 THURSDAY
Moon Age Day 19   Moon Sign Aries

The demands of your life make little indulgences less than likely at the moment. Circumstances force you into the limelight, a position you may not relish today. Don't be too quick to judge people or situations at this time and listen very carefully to the thoughts of your partner.

31 FRIDAY
Moon Age Day 20   Moon Sign Aries

Avoid allowing yourself to be dominated by emotional impulses, particularly since many of them are actually unnecessary. You need to free yourself from old habits, especially ones that you know are bad for you. With a forward-looking attitude later in the day, a greater feeling of contentment emerges.

September

2018

Your Month at a Glance

(+) = Opportunities are around   ● = Be on the defensive   = Life is pretty ordinary

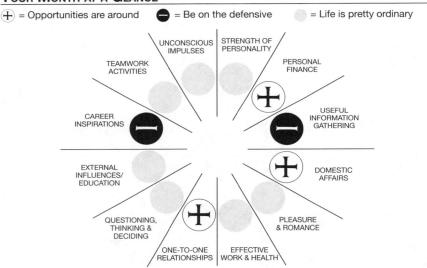

UNCONSCIOUS IMPULSES

STRENGTH OF PERSONALITY

TEAMWORK ACTIVITIES

PERSONAL FINANCE

CAREER INSPIRATIONS

USEFUL INFORMATION GATHERING

EXTERNAL INFLUENCES/ EDUCATION

DOMESTIC AFFAIRS

QUESTIONING, THINKING & DECIDING

PLEASURE & ROMANCE

ONE-TO-ONE RELATIONSHIPS

EFFECTIVE WORK & HEALTH

September Highs and Lows

Here I show you how the rhythms of the Moon will affect you this month. Like the tide, your energies and abilities will rise and fall with its pattern. When it is above the centre line, go for it, when it is below, you should be resting.

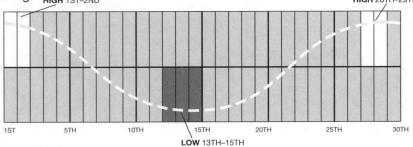

HIGH 1ST–2ND

HIGH 28TH–29TH

1ST   5TH   10TH   15TH   20TH   25TH   30TH

LOW 13TH–15TH

1 SATURDAY
Moon Age Day 21   Moon Sign Taurus

A very relaxed pace prevails today and it may well occur to you that some of the stresses that have surrounded you of late appear to be self-created. Conflict is likely in personal relationships, unless you stop to analyse what others are actually saying, though such situations don't have the power to shake your present equilibrium.

2 SUNDAY
Moon Age Day 22   Moon Sign Taurus

There is much to be said for doing things in twos and everything to gain from sharing the best of what you are. It is one-to-one relationships that seem to hold the most magical possibilities at this stage of the weekend, even though it could seem at first today that you are going to be more or less fully committed to practicalities.

3 MONDAY
Moon Age Day 23   Moon Sign Gemini

Not everyone appears to have your best interests at heart but they should come good when it matters the most. Don't be too quick to judge the actions of people you don't know well. Your mind is working overtime and it seems easy for you to assess how almost anyone is likely to behave under given circumstances – but you could be wrong.

4 TUESDAY
Moon Age Day 24   Moon Sign Gemini

There is a great deal of superficiality in recent astrological trends and you could be feeling that your need for intimacy is not being addressed as much as you would wish. If it seems as though something is missing from your life right now you might want to spend more time reaching out to people in a personal sense.

5 WEDNESDAY
Moon Age Day 25   Moon Sign Cancer

Your ideas are quite far-reaching now and you have the verbal dexterity to put them across to others. Press ahead with major ambitions and do whatever you can to make certain others notice you are present. That shouldn't be at all hard under present trends and nor will be making a good impression during any sort of social function.

6 THURSDAY
Moon Age Day 26   Moon Sign Cancer

Progress in a career sense may now depend on your ability to think on your feet. That shouldn't be much of a problem for Taurus right now, but you could be up against some fairly determined characters. When it matters the most, the planets assist you to make the sort of friends who prove to be very supportive, so build on this trend whereever possible.

7 FRIDAY
Moon Age Day 27   Moon Sign Leo

Your powers of creativity look especially good now, and you will also discover that your organisational skills are more noteworthy at this time. Your role in group activities is quite well emphasised at this stage of the month. You should be feeling optimistic and able to push yourself in all sorts of ways that turn out to be useful.

8 SATURDAY
Moon Age Day 28   Moon Sign Leo

Keep your eyes open because encounters with those you feel to be on the same wavelength as you should prove very rewarding indeed and could bring you to a better understanding of situations that have confused you in the past. Don't stick around in the same place today and do what you can to travel around a little.

9 SUNDAY
Moon Age Day 0   Moon Sign Virgo

It won't be possible to agree with everyone and you will be much better off once you have committed yourself one way or another. Trust your own judgement in most matters, both business and personal. Don't sit on the fence today. You will need to take a stance, even if this means being slightly unpopular with someone.

10 MONDAY
Moon Age Day 1   Moon Sign Virgo

You might have to ask yourself if you have been aiming too high in some instances. If the answer is yes, be prepared to modify your position. A plan of action might have to be postponed or even abandoned altogether. There is time to think now and this should help you to see at least some situations in a very different light.

11 TUESDAY
Moon Age Day 2   Moon Sign Libra

Travel and intellectual interests come together to create an interesting interlude at this stage of the working week. Today would be fine for pleasing yourself and you might wish to put aside a part of the day to visit somewhere interesting. It doesn't have to be any further than your local park or museum because it is the change that matters.

12 WEDNESDAY
Moon Age Day 3   Moon Sign Libra

It's possible that your relatives might feel that they have a special hold over you today, and could be making great demands on your time. Out there in the wider world, actions speak louder than words, a fact you understand all too well as a rule. The approval of your peers is quite important to you at this time and you will be doing all you can to please everyone.

13 THURSDAY
Moon Age Day 4   Moon Sign Scorpio

You may have to work hard today to accommodate those you really don't like, and to disguise the fact from both them and yourself. The seesaw that is life is in operation again, bringing with it a short period during which the charm you have been showing of late takes something of a holiday.

14 FRIDAY
Moon Age Day 5   Moon Sign Scorpio

It would be best to pace yourself and work according to plans you laid down some time ago, rather than trying to make up the rules as you go along. It's important that others know the way you are likely to react, so that they can help you out if needed. Most Taureans will want all the support they can get today.

15 SATURDAY
Moon Age Day 6   Moon Sign Scorpio

Although it appears that others are getting on better than you are, this is little more than an illusion to which you are clinging. You really do need to look at matters with a longer-term perspective and not get carried away by the events of any one day. Keep up your efforts to get ahead in your social world.

16 SUNDAY
Moon Age Day 7   Moon Sign Sagittarius

Sunday brings a slight slowing of the pace, though certainly not for long. In a social and personal sense you might not even notice a change of momentum. True, you will be pleased to luxuriate somewhat, and you won't take kindly to being overwhelmed with work at the present time.

17 MONDAY
Moon Age Day 8   Moon Sign Sagittarius

For today you seem to be enjoying a fairly nostalgic period and tend to be looking back as much as you are looking gaze forward. As long as you realise that the past offers lessons for the future, all is well. What you don't want right now is the contemplation of some Utopia that never really existed.

18 TUESDAY
Moon Age Day 9   Moon Sign Capricorn

You might feel that the pressure is somehow on in terms of relationships. This fact could show itself in any one of a number of different ways. Perhaps family members are more demanding, or your partner is worrying about certain issues. Whatever turns up, deal with it steadily and don't panic.

19 WEDNESDAY
Moon Age Day 10   Moon Sign Capricorn

You are the most entertaining of all the zodiac signs to have around today. Intent on improving the lot of your family and friends, you show a very sociable face to the world at large. Even strangers will be uplifted by your general attitude and should be reacting to you in a very positive way.

20 THURSDAY
Moon Age Day 11   Moon Sign Aquarius

It is clear now that you will want to be on the move. Whether this means an autumn holiday, or merely a trip out of some sort, make the most of any good weather that remains and don't stick around at home. You may feel the need to be in the company of stimulating people and to get the most from new contacts.

21 FRIDAY
Moon Age Day 12   Moon Sign Aquarius

Stand by for a busy period of comings and goings. There won't be quite the amount of time to stop and think about specifics that you would wish but that doesn't mean you should avoid taking any sort of action. You can't have everything you want today, but you can at least get part of the way down the road to contentment.

22 SATURDAY
Moon Age Day 13   Moon Sign Aquarius

Along comes a day when you will prefer, and possibly even benefit from, your own company. Revolutionary ideas come into your mind and there isn't much doubt about your ability to concentrate on detailed tasks. The fact that you are not the life and soul of the party at the moment need not be a great cause of concern.

23 SUNDAY
Moon Age Day 14   Moon Sign Pisces

You could so easily find yourself in a prominent position today, so you will need to keep your wits about you. Being in the limelight is a double-edged sword for Taurus – you often like it but sometimes hate it also. Fortunately, trends suggest that you are not feeling particularly shy at present.

24 MONDAY
Moon Age Day 15   Moon Sign Pisces

A productive and generally positive time in terms of stability makes itself obvious for much of the early part of this week. Although this may mean that you show a marked preference to remain in one place, it does please you to realise that your life is fully in order. What you hear in casual conversations needs some careful thinking about now.

25 TUESDAY
Moon Age Day 16   Moon Sign Aries

The pace of everyday life is clearly quite rapid at present, so much so that you don't really have time to stop and take a breath. Be clear and specific when in conversation with others because if there is something you want, you need to ask for it plainly. Most people will respect your present honesty and integrity.

26 WEDNESDAY
Moon Age Day 17   Moon Sign Aries

Issues of personality do put you on the spot today, meaning that you cannot hide in the shadows regarding any situation you feel particularly strongly about. Don't be afraid to speak your mind if you fear – or know – that others won't agree with your point of view. If you explain yourself, you can win out in the end.

27 THURSDAY
Moon Age Day 18   Moon Sign Aries

Your chart today indicates that emotional matters can put you in the hot seat, so try to avoid this by explaining yourself right from the start. As long as you are being genuinely honest, all is well. What won't work right now is attempting to fool others, even if you are simply trying to avoid hurting them.

28 FRIDAY
Moon Age Day 19   Moon Sign Taurus

Things change quickly as the lunar high begins to take hold of your life. Any timidity that could have been evident yesterday now disappears altogether, leaving you feeling extra confident and anxious to make a big impression. That shouldn't be difficult, especially in a social sense.

29 SATURDAY
Moon Age Day 20   Moon Sign Taurus

This is another day that appears to be geared, fundamentally, towards personal success. You are chattier than usual, and willing to put your point of view across to just about anyone who is willing to listen. This means superiors at work, too, and the impression you make will not be wasted.

30 SUNDAY
Moon Age Day 21   Moon Sign Gemini

Lively discussions seem to be the order of the day at the very end of September. Keep your comments on any situation brief but honest and you won't go far wrong. Feelings of excitement might be somewhat justified by the promise of even better times to come, so you can afford to be optimistic.

October

2018

Your Month at a Glance

(+) = Opportunities are around (−) = Be on the defensive ● = Life is pretty ordinary

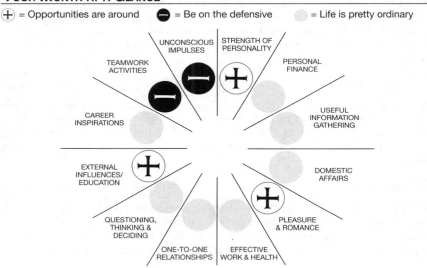

October Highs and Lows

Here I show you how the rhythms of the Moon will affect you this month. Like the tide, your energies and abilities will rise and fall with its pattern. When it is above the centre line, go for it, when it is below, you should be resting.

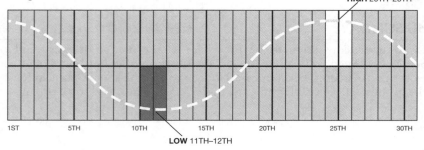

1 MONDAY
Moon Age Day 22   Moon Sign Gemini

Don't be surprised if some romantic overtures are coming your way at any time now. Most of these will come from expected directions. Avenues of communication now tend to open up after a few days when some Taureans may have felt quieter or more restricted in social situations, so make the most of this.

2 TUESDAY
Moon Age Day 23   Moon Sign Cancer

In the main you present a very humorous face to the world at large and there are likely to be many laughs along the way. Taurus occasionally takes itself rather more seriously than it should, though this definitely isn't the case now. Your thinking and the way you communicate are positive.

3 WEDNESDAY
Moon Age Day 24   Moon Sign Cancer

Getting to grips with family issues should be easy and you will also find sufficient time for romance to work one or two little wonders in your life. House and home suddenly appear very important, creating the right circumstances for a happy but deliberately family-focused sort of middle to the working week.

4 THURSDAY
Moon Age Day 25   Moon Sign Leo

Even casual friends can be particularly warm right now and there could be some surprising news arriving from the direction of a really close pal. Personal relationships should be working extremely well for you and some Taureans should be finding themselves at the start of exciting new romances.

5 FRIDAY
Moon Age Day 26   Moon Sign Leo

Organising yourself might prove a little awkward today, though mainly in a humorous way. You have a tendency to be just a little absent-minded under present trends. You are most likely happily on the go for most of today, with travel once again positively highlighted and an ability to make gains in new places.

6 SATURDAY
Moon Age Day 27   Moon Sign Virgo

Take a fresh look at old issues and be willing to address a point of view that is rather different from the one you might generally adopt yourself. You can put the force of your personality to good use right now, even though strictly professional or practical matters probably will not be on the agenda. This is Saturday after all.

7 SUNDAY
Moon Age Day 28   Moon Sign Virgo

Make this Sunday your own by getting out of the house with relatives or friends and by seeking to push the margins of the possible. Your social life and group ventures generally are important at this stage and you should do everything within your power in order to enjoy yourself as much as you can.

8 MONDAY
Moon Age Day 29   Moon Sign Virgo

There are good prospects for travel today, and it also appears that at work you now have more power at your fingertips and a better idea of how you should go about important tasks. People will call upon you for your special support. The more you get done today the better is your chance of enjoying some relaxation later in the week.

9 TUESDAY
Moon Age Day 0   Moon Sign Libra

There are gains to be made on the financial front but you will need to be careful about investing any sum of money and consider all the options before you take any action. Friends should be very supportive and extremely loyal at this time. It won't be hard for you to trust people and you can rely on your intuition when it comes to sorting out the wheat from the chaff in any social situation.

10 WEDNESDAY
Moon Age Day 1   Moon Sign Libra

Your confidence remains high enough when you are dealing with practical matters but you could be just slightly below par in your search for absolute personal happiness. Some positive benefits may arise from groups and partnerships. Although you do not always mix absolutely freely with the world at large, you will do so more readily now.

11 THURSDAY
Moon Age Day 2   Moon Sign Scorpio

Your enthusiasm is likely to flag now that the lunar low is around. This means that you won't be as optimistic as life and circumstances actually deserve. If you have to spend some money now in order to save later, then this is the course of action you should take. In social relationships avoid pushing matters to breaking point – there's really no need.

12 FRIDAY
Moon Age Day 3   Moon Sign Scorpio

It's time to slow down and take stock. If there are any jobs you really don't feel like doing today, leave them for later. Taking a well-earned break is no sin and you will work that much harder after the lunar low is gone. The attitudes of both family members and friends could be difficult to fathom today.

13 SATURDAY
Moon Age Day 4   Moon Sign Sagittarius

Things could get more exciting now. Your ideas and even what might once have seemed your most outrageous schemes can find good support from others today. This is partly because you are explaining yourself so well and you won't have any difficulty persuading people that you are quite a specialist in some ways. Keep abreast of current affairs.

14 SUNDAY
Moon Age Day 5   Moon Sign Sagittarius

Be gentle on yourself today. You won't get very far if you insist on trying to get ahead by sheer force. The force of your own perosnality provides all that is necessary to see you achieving more or less anything you want, but this is not a time for forcing issues. Taurus is very considerate of relatives and friends at this time.

15 MONDAY
Moon Age Day 6   Moon Sign Capricorn

It may now be possible to confront an issue that you have tried to avoid in the past, and this might be much easier than you had been expecting. Get jobs you don't like out of the way early. You should be especially pleased with your social life and with friendships, because both offer you diversion and interest today.

16 TUESDAY
Moon Age Day 7   Moon Sign Capricorn

Your luck with money certainly doesn't appear to have run out. Venus is now strong in your chart and ought to be reasonably supportive in financial terms. There are also possible gains on the work front. Some relationships need a new approach, which necessitates a change of attitude on your part.

17 WEDNESDAY
Moon Age Day 8   Moon Sign Capricorn

Consolidation seems to be the key to getting on well right now. Instead of firing off with new ideas, look carefully at the ones you have been addressing recently. It might take only a very small amount of effort to put the seal on weeks or months of work. On the way through life today new friends are a possibility.

18 THURSDAY
Moon Age Day 9   Moon Sign Aquarius

There is a powerful indication in your chart that money-making will rise to the forefront of your mind around this time. It may be for this reason that your associations with others are taking second place. If everything is firmly in place regarding the details of your life, your ability to make cash along the way goes without saying.

19 FRIDAY
Moon Age Day 10   Moon Sign Aquarius

The planetary emphasis now pushes you in the direction of work and property. That means you are taking less notice of friendship. This could be something of a mistake because there are definitely people around you now who want to get closer to you. With these contacts comes a whole new way of looking at certain matters.

20 SATURDAY
Moon Age Day 11   Moon Sign Pisces

Minor unexpected pressures are brought to bear on you now. These can do little to stem the general progress that surrounds you at present, though they could slow you down somewhat. Take care when dealing with younger family members, some of whom are far too sensitive for their own good.

21 SUNDAY
Moon Age Day 12   Moon Sign Pisces

This is a time during which love life and relationships should be putting a very definite smile on your face. If you don't have the time to do everything you wish in a practical sense, be willing to leave some of it for another day. Most of the people you meet today prove to be very reasonable.

22 MONDAY
Moon Age Day 13   Moon Sign Pisces

Don't believe everything you hear today because there are some unreliable types around. Mostly, these will be people who are charming and quite incapable of doing you any harm, but you need to be on your guard all the same. Trends also suggest a slight tendency towards mysterious little illnesses.

23 TUESDAY
Moon Age Day 14   Moon Sign Aries

Work and practical affairs keep you generally busy today and offer you the comfort of knowing that life is running in a smooth and steady way. There probably won't be too much in the way of excitement, though you are hardly likely to be put off by that fact at the moment.

24 WEDNESDAY
Moon Age Day 15   Moon Sign Aries

Although you are feeling quite assertive today, you do need to watch your step in some ways. Not everyone is working towards your ultimate good, no matter what they say to the contrary. Problems are not likely to arise with relatives or friends, though colleagues could be more of a problem.

25 THURSDAY
Moon Age Day 16   Moon Sign Taurus

Everything should be a laugh today and even situations you once found hard going are dealt with in a flash. Most of the people you meet seem to be naturally compromising in their attitudes but much of this has to do with the way you are feeling yourself. Your high spirits are evident, as is your sense of humour.

26 FRIDAY
Moon Age Day 17   Moon Sign Taurus

This is the time of the month during which you can afford to test your luck. The gains that can come along today could surpass your expectations and you certainly do need to make quick decisions if you want to make the very best of life. Confidence is written through you in a way that really shows.

27 SATURDAY
Moon Age Day 18   Moon Sign Gemini

Right now you have the knack of getting your point of view across in a very positive way and can really get on famously when in the company of people whose attitude stimulates you in any way. Frank, free and quite outspoken, you can definitely make today your own with only a little effort.

28 SUNDAY
Moon Age Day 19   Moon Sign Gemini

Now your acquisitive tendencies are strong, which isn't so strange for the zodiac sign of Taurus. You know what you want from life, and have a pretty good idea about how you intend to get it. Some would call you calculating, but since you bear the good of others in mind, this isn't really the case.

29 MONDAY
Moon Age Day 20   Moon Sign Cancer

Socially speaking, there are one or two individuals who could let you down today, which is why it would be sensible to check and double check all details. This is also true with regard to travel. Journeys at the moment might have to be postponed, or rearranged at the last minute.

30 TUESDAY
Moon Age Day 21   Moon Sign Cancer

There is likely to be a good deal of nostalgia in the air at this time. Looking back is fine, just as long as you don't always use aspects of the past as a yardstick for what is happening now. Times change and you alter with them. Keep an open mind about the behaviour and attitudes of younger family members.

31 WEDNESDAY

Moon Age Day 22   Moon Sign Cancer

Career issues should prove to be quite fulfilling. However, there are certain actions that you should be taking yourself in order to get ahead of the game. If people are not pulling their weight to the extent that you think is necessary, now is the time to remind them of the fact. Meanwhile, put in that extra bit of effort yourself.

November

2018

YOUR MONTH AT A GLANCE

➕ = Opportunities are around   ➖ = Be on the defensive   ⬤ = Life is pretty ordinary

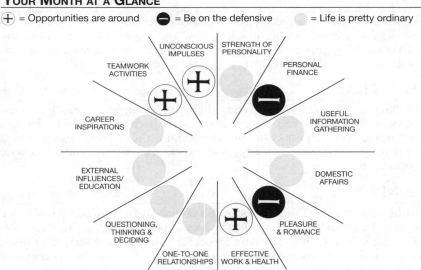

UNCONSCIOUS IMPULSES

STRENGTH OF PERSONALITY

TEAMWORK ACTIVITIES

PERSONAL FINANCE

CAREER INSPIRATIONS

USEFUL INFORMATION GATHERING

EXTERNAL INFLUENCES/ EDUCATION

DOMESTIC AFFAIRS

QUESTIONING, THINKING & DECIDING

PLEASURE & ROMANCE

ONE-TO-ONE RELATIONSHIPS

EFFECTIVE WORK & HEALTH

NOVEMBER HIGHS AND LOWS

Here I show you how the rhythms of the Moon will affect you this month. Like the tide, your energies and abilities will rise and fall with its pattern. When it is above the centre line, go for it, when it is below, you should be resting.

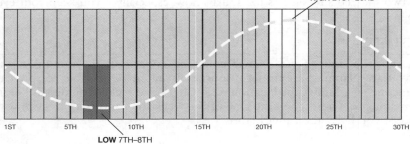

HIGH 21ST–23RD

1ST   5TH   10TH   15TH   20TH   25TH   30TH

LOW 7TH–8TH

1 THURSDAY
Moon Age Day 23   Moon Sign Leo

There is help around if you want it, though you tend to be rather insular on occasions at the moment and might even think that to ask for assistance is beneath your dignity. A rather thorny problem could arise today and you need to be fairly circumspect in the way you choose to deal with it. You do have confidence – but you have to seek it within yourself.

2 FRIDAY
Moon Age Day 24   Moon Sign Leo

Friday brings a more energetic phase and the chance to get ahead, particularly at work. You are not lacking in know-how and might think up a new way to do something important. Be aware that people are watching you today, though in a very positive manner, so put your best foot forward.

3 SATURDAY
Moon Age Day 25   Moon Sign Virgo

Be willing to compromise today and others will relinquish a great deal of the control of situations to you. Taurus may not see itself as a natural leader, but those around you respect both your views and actions. This is likely to be a time that proves to be particularly good for social adventures and for general co-operation.

4 SUNDAY
Moon Age Day 26   Moon Sign Virgo

Getting on with others should not be difficult today but you could find some people to be rather less decisive than you would wish. Don't try to please too many people because it simply won't work. It might be necessary to let those you love make their own mistakes since it is probably the only way they will learn valuable lessons.

5 MONDAY
Moon Age Day 27   Moon Sign Libra

Those in authority tend to be on your side at the start of this new working week and you should also find friends being especially helpful. Concentrate on a specific matter early in the day and generalities later. There could be one or two shortcuts to success for Taurus now, especially if you keep your eyes open.

6 TUESDAY
Moon Age Day 28   Moon Sign Libra

Despite the time of year, travel could be uppermost in your mind and if you are planning a long-term journey it might be sensible to speak to someone who knows the location well. Check and recheck all details before you embark. This is the best time of the week for conversation, even with people you have never met before.

7 WEDNESDAY
Moon Age Day 0   Moon Sign Scorpio

The attitudes and opinions of those you are dealing with on a daily basis might surprise or even shock you later in the day but don't let on that this is the case. Keep your expectations of life realistic and the chances are that the lunar low won't have too much of a bearing on your life at this time.

8 THURSDAY
Moon Age Day 1   Moon Sign Scorpio

Progress may be steady at best because you have the lunar low to contend with today. This might not appear to be too much of a drag because you have been constantly on the go for a while now. All Taureans need rest and recuperation at some stage because that is what gets you thinking and planning.

9 FRIDAY
Moon Age Day 2   Moon Sign Sagittarius

Avoid family disputes and it might be sensible to spend as much time as you can with people to whom you are not related at all. Although you could suffer from a slight lack of inspiration early in the day, it won't be long before you are feeling much more positive and really getting stuck into things.

10 SATURDAY
Moon Age Day 3   Moon Sign Sagittarius

Not everyone appears to have your best interests at heart but it is possible that in a few cases you are misinterpreting the situation. A better day for finances is possible, perhaps with some unexpected gains. Group events give today an air of excitement and it is very easy for you to join in and have fun.

11 SUNDAY
Moon Age Day 4   Moon Sign Sagittarius

Not everyone shares your opinions at the moment but you are not likely to contradict anyone today. It looks as though you are keeping yourself very much to yourself. You won't be thinking big because present trends favour the smaller world-view that comes over Taurus on occasions. Money matters should be variable but generally stable.

12 MONDAY
Moon Age Day 5   Moon Sign Capricorn

Visits to family members or even friends you don't see very often might prove to be especially rewarding and you seem to be in a particularly social frame of mind all of a sudden. The conversations you have with others around this time tend to be pleasant and sympathetic in both directions.

13 TUESDAY
Moon Age Day 6   Moon Sign Capricorn

It is in a professional sense that the competitive qualities of your nature are on display. You need this hard edge on occasions, but it's impossible domestically right now. Enjoy the fact that you can take a different and more stimulating approach in discussions at work, while those at home are somehow sugar-coated at the moment.

14 WEDNESDAY
Moon Age Day 7   Moon Sign Aquarius

In love and relationships you need to use your intuition today. Perhaps your partner is not behaving as you have come to expect or else the object of your devotion still isn't noticing you? There's more than one way to skin a cat and when it comes to being slightly devious, you have what it takes at the moment. Use your powers of communication as they are looking good.

15 THURSDAY
Moon Age Day 8   Moon Sign Aquarius

The really positive part of today is likely to come along once your commitments in the practical world are out of the way. Meanwhile a change in planetary emphasis today means inevitable alterations to your working schedules. Not all of these look potentially good but will probably work out better than you expect.

16 FRIDAY
Moon Age Day 9   Moon Sign Aquarius

Taking a very serious attitude to almost anything right now could turn out to be something of a mistake. The more off-the-wall you appear to be at present, the greater is the attention you get. Exercise a little caution because certain important changes you have been gradually making to your life might now come temporarily unstuck.

17 SATURDAY ☿
Moon Age Day 10   Moon Sign Pisces

Everyday life is apt to be pleasant and rewarding, with personal relationships offering the best possibilities of all this Saturday. You can make life go with a swing for family members, and most of all for your partner. It should also be possible to speculate rather more than you have been doing earlier in the week, with caution of course.

18 SUNDAY ☿
Moon Age Day 11   Moon Sign Pisces

Challenges, or even confrontations, in your closest personal relationships may threaten to shake your equilibrium somewhat. This is only really an issue if you allow yourself to be drawn in. Try to remain patient, even in the face of criticism, and all should be well. On a positive note, your finances could be strengthening at this time.

19 MONDAY ☿   *Moon Age Day 12   Moon Sign Aries*

A fairly nostalgic day is certain now, with time also for reflection on happenings early in the month. Once again it is particularly important not to dwell on things that have been and gone. If you are using your view of past events in order to explain your present activities, there is a strong chance that you are not committing yourself fully.

20 TUESDAY ☿   *Moon Age Day 13   Moon Sign Aries*

Although you are intellectually quicker than ever, there are still one or two people around who seem to want to fool you in some way. This is going to be difficult for them to achieve because you are clearly on the ball and attentive today. Make the most of this time to ring the changes socially and personally.

21 WEDNESDAY ☿   *Moon Age Day 14   Moon Sign Taurus*

This is a good time to push your luck and certainly not a period during which you should hide your abilities or your intentions. Allow your light to shine brightly and have confidence in your ability to get things done. Financial trends are especially good, as are the romantic prospects of this positive day.

22 THURSDAY ☿   *Moon Age Day 15   Moon Sign Taurus*

Your confidence is greatly increased and there is no doubt about your desire to get ahead. This may not be immediately obvious at work but you are very good at mixing business with pleasure right now. Ideal situations might just happen by themselves – but a little push from you won't do any harm either.

23 FRIDAY ☿   *Moon Age Day 16   Moon Sign Taurus*

A new boost to your romantic life comes along now. Concentrate more on the relationship that you have with your partner and spend time in their company. If this is difficult on account of work commitments, you can at least find some moments later in the day to let those you love know how much you care.

24 SATURDAY ☿   *Moon Age Day 17   Moon Sign Gemini*

Some setbacks could be unavoidable today. It would be best not to bite off more than you can chew and to allow your friends and colleagues to do some jobs on your behalf. There is nothing at all wrong with looking ahead and doing a little careful planning, whilst at the same time getting some rest.

25 SUNDAY ☿ *Moon Age Day 18   Moon Sign Gemini*

Friendship and group encounters generally appear to have a great deal going for them right now. What they provide is a platform for your ego, perhaps at a time when you are not quite as confident in yourself as has been the case of late. Make time to socialise, particularly by the evening.

26 MONDAY ☿ *Moon Age Day 19   Moon Sign Cancer*

Today you find a positive emphasis being placed on material considerations. This is the sort of month November is turning out to be for you and you take great delight in new possessions. Don't forget before you spend money that Christmas is not that far away.

27 TUESDAY ☿ *Moon Age Day 20   Moon Sign Cancer*

After a somewhat busy period, you might be feeling slightly overtaxed and will probably be pleased enough to have a restful day or two. Whether things turn out that way really depends on how willing you are to allow others to take some of the strain. Actually, it might be churlish to prevent them.

28 WEDNESDAY ☿ *Moon Age Day 21   Moon Sign Leo*

At work, someone may be putting you in the picture regarding an issue that has been at the forefront of your mind of late. Getting to know what is going on in your vicinity seems especially important now, which is why you are listening so carefully to everything that is being said.

29 THURSDAY ☿ *Moon Age Day 22   Moon Sign Leo*

You have little real patience with certain emotional matters today and you may consider that someone you know well is acting in a fairly irrational manner. There are some unusual people about, whose ideas and actions could fascinate you somewhat, but don't be drawn into anything weird.

30 FRIDAY ☿ *Moon Age Day 23   Moon Sign Virgo*

The domestic atmosphere is likely to become livelier, with much communication taking place and a possible visit from relatives or friends. For today you can expect a number of surprises and unbidden events, all of which contribute to a general increase in interest and participation on your part.

December

2018

YOUR MONTH AT A GLANCE

(+) = Opportunities are around   ➖ = Be on the defensive   ⬤ = Life is pretty ordinary

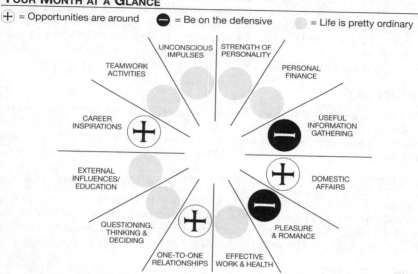

UNCONSCIOUS IMPULSES

STRENGTH OF PERSONALITY

TEAMWORK ACTIVITIES

PERSONAL FINANCE

CAREER INSPIRATIONS

USEFUL INFORMATION GATHERING

EXTERNAL INFLUENCES/ EDUCATION

DOMESTIC AFFAIRS

QUESTIONING, THINKING & DECIDING

PLEASURE & ROMANCE

ONE-TO-ONE RELATIONSHIPS

EFFECTIVE WORK & HEALTH

DECEMBER HIGHS AND LOWS

Here I show you how the rhythms of the Moon will affect you this month. Like the tide, your energies and abilities will rise and fall with its pattern. When it is above the centre line, go for it, when it is below, you should be resting.

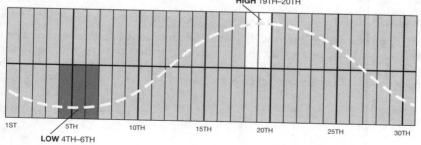

HIGH 19TH–20TH

1ST   5TH   10TH   15TH   20TH   25TH   30TH

LOW 4TH–6TH

1 SATURDAY ☿ *Moon Age Day 24 Moon Sign Virgo*

Spend time with family members and do what you can to support a friend who could well be going through a rough phase right now. You are well aware of the elements of your life that deserve your attention, even though one or two people might think that they know different.

2 SUNDAY ☿ *Moon Age Day 25 Moon Sign Libra*

Well ahead of the holiday season this could be as good a time as any to analyse what you have achieved during the last year and to make new plans for beyond the end of December. Certainly, you are likely to have the time to do so, on what could prove to be a somewhat quieter day. Trends do suggest, though, that you haven't seen for a long time could come back into your life.

3 MONDAY ☿ *Moon Age Day 26 Moon Sign Libra*

For many Taureans the time is right for a short break from obligations. Maybe you have some time off work, or at least are relinquishing a few of the responsibilities that you would normally take on. For whatever reason, you have the chance for a steadier day, and will probably grab it with both hands.

4 TUESDAY ☿ *Moon Age Day 27 Moon Sign Scorpio*

Get ready for a couple of days during which it will be difficult to get everything you want from life. The lunar low is holding you back, but not all that much. As long as you stick to planning, and leave a few of the more concrete jobs until the back end of the week, you will hardly be held up at all this month.

5 WEDNESDAY ☿ *Moon Age Day 28 Moon Sign Scorpio*

You are trying very hard to swim against a tide that really will not turn in your favour. Maybe it should have occurred to you by now that this is a complete waste of time and effort. Let someone else take the strain for the moment, whilst you sit back and enjoy yourself. Taurus can enjoy a really clear conscience now.

6 THURSDAY ☿ *Moon Age Day 29 Moon Sign Scorpio*

You won't be very pleased with yourself if situations become confused or if you are not keeping up with the expectations others have of you. In a more general sense, you ought to be feeling quite positive about life. The main thing today is keeping on top of organisational issues.

7 FRIDAY
Moon Age Day 0   Moon Sign Sagittarius

Certain planetary trends show this to be a time during which Taurus becomes fascinated by the way things work. Some experimentation is called for, if only to satisfy your curiosity. The spirit of teamwork is stronger in you today and your ability to get on well with the world at large is more noticeable.

8 SATURDAY
Moon Age Day 1   Moon Sign Sagittarius

It might be necessary to fend off one or two social invitations today, if only because you can't do everything. Gathering together all the relevant information you need should be child's play now. You are particularly well organised at the moment, which is probably why others turn to you when they need sorting out.

9 SUNDAY
Moon Age Day 2   Moon Sign Capricorn

It could just be that you feel you cannot break through the carefully created shell of a colleague or friend. However, there are great rewards to be had from even the most mundane aspects of life, even if you have to look at matters carefully and use a good deal of intuition to get the best from any situation.

10 MONDAY
Moon Age Day 3   Moon Sign Capricorn

A sense of variety and freedom is both important and appealing to Taureans at this time. Don't be a stick-in-the-mud. Although this might not be exactly the season for outdoor activities, you could find the call of the wild appealing. Later in the day, you might choose to spend at least some time alone.

11 TUESDAY
Moon Age Day 4   Moon Sign Aquarius

The present emphasis falls on finances, probably not surprising at this expensive time of the year. You are quite canny at the moment and know full well how to get value for money. Even at this stage, there could be one or two things available for Christmas that you get at rock bottom prices.

12 WEDNESDAY
Moon Age Day 5   Moon Sign Aquarius

Be willing to take a few chances and to push the bounds of credibility when it comes to your own ideas. Romance looms large in your thinking and compliments are not hard to come by. Although you might feel that your influence over everyday matters is rather limited, you would probably be wrong.

13 THURSDAY
Moon Age Day 6   Moon Sign Aquarius

For many Taureans, the greatest joy of today comes from your love life, which is likely to be as enjoyable as you would wish. Something you have done for someone else in the past is now paid back with dividends. Expecting the best of others is worthwhile at present since they are unlikely to let you down.

14 FRIDAY
Moon Age Day 7   Moon Sign Pisces

Along comes a happy period during which you should find yourself to be the centre of attention. Although such a situation would sometimes cause embarrassment to the Taurus nature, that isn't at all the case now. Avoid confusion in your associations with others by simply speaking your mind with candour.

15 SATURDAY
Moon Age Day 8   Moon Sign Pisces

Try to avoid needless arguments with your friends. Even if people seem to be in the most intractable frame of mind you don't have to join in. Make this a Saturday to remember by doing something different. If this turns out to be a problem, look to your most exciting and original friend for ideas.

16 SUNDAY
Moon Age Day 9   Moon Sign Pisces

There are new and interesting people around and they seem to come along at just the right time as far as you are concerned. There may be tasks to do today that you like the look of at all. All the same, you should avoid putting them off because you might be making a rod for your own back later.

17 MONDAY
Moon Age Day 10   Moon Sign Aries

What an excellent day this would be for getting something new up and running. Positive trends seem to be assisting in most of your efforts and there could also be financial gains, both expected and surprising. You can call on a creative mood and lightness of touch just when you need it the most.

18 TUESDAY
Moon Age Day 11   Moon Sign Aries

You score many points in social situations, particularly if you are away from home and enjoying the hospitality of others. Try not to be critical about the way those around you arrange their functions and simply pitch in. Too much fussing won't get you anywhere today so try to stay very relaxed.

19 WEDNESDAY
Moon Age Day 12   Moon Sign Taurus

Almost never will you notice the onset of the lunar high more than appears to be the case today. Things have been quite up and down across the last week or so, but it's plain today that you are ready for action and quite keen to get ahead. Don't worry about how you do things, simply get stuck in.

20 THURSDAY
Moon Age Day 13   Moon Sign Taurus

This is when you reach your mental and physical peak, just in time for the last run-up to Christmas. It doesn't matter what you take on today, you have the energy and determination to see it through properly. Gains can be made as a result of meetings and discussions that could have taken place some time ago.

21 FRIDAY
Moon Age Day 14   Moon Sign Gemini

You may be in two minds about certain issues today, especially those connected with work. If this turns out to be the case you really need to use your intuition, which is working well at this time. Avoid getting into any sort of difficulty by varying your routines and also by thinking about things in different ways.

22 SATURDAY
Moon Age Day 15   Moon Sign Gemini

Financially speaking, there could be some minor improvements on the horizon now, and not a moment too soon with Christmas so close. Nevertheless, you need to spend wisely and to look out for those bargains that lie around every corner. All in all, this could be one of the best days of December for shopping.

23 SUNDAY
Moon Age Day 16   Moon Sign Cancer

You may be feeling quite restless today, though it would be difficult for you to know exactly why this state of affairs has come about. You could blame any number of possibilities but that is no excuse for not treating others properly. Get rid of your own strange thoughts by concentrating on the lives of those around you.

24 MONDAY
Moon Age Day 17   Moon Sign Cancer

You should definitely be enjoying a high profile on this Christmas Eve. Despite the fact that you register how much still has to be done, you must find ways in which you can enjoy yourself. If you keep slogging away for the whole of the day you will be left with the impression that everyone is having fun at your expense.

25 TUESDAY
Moon Age Day 18   Moon Sign Leo

In all probability you will enjoy an extremely interesting and varied sort of Christmas Day. It could be that not everyone in your family and friendship circle is having quite as good a time as you are and this might lead to extra effort on your part. The most enjoyable associations today come via close, personal attachments.

26 WEDNESDAY
Moon Age Day 19   Moon Sign Leo

Almost everyone wants your attention at the same time today. The personal need to be busy and active might run contrary to all the festive celebrations now. What you need to do is compartmentalise your time, making sure that you have at least some moments left to spend with your partner and with family members.

27 THURSDAY
Moon Age Day 20   Moon Sign Virgo

Affairs of the heart are well highlighted in your chart today, as is travel, perhaps to see people you haven't shared an hour or two with for quite a long time. Although you might be bullied into doing things that go against the grain, you could be quite surprised with how they turn out in the end. It is worth putting yourself out.

28 FRIDAY
Moon Age Day 21   Moon Sign Virgo

Now it appears you are in such a hurry to get things done, you are forgetting some of the most important details. If you want to avoid having to stop, and then begin all over again, concentrate fully on the task at hand. Friends are there to lend a helping hand if you offer them the chance to do so.

29 SATURDAY
Moon Age Day 22   Moon Sign Libra

This is far from being a normal sort of Saturday as far as you are concerned, even if you have to work. When you are not busy, there are gains to be made through love and new friendship. Your social instincts are very definitely engaged today and you can be the best company imaginable. You not only join in but should be happy to organise things too.

30 SUNDAY
Moon Age Day 23   Moon Sign Libra

With the positive emphasis this Sunday on your inner self, and maybe also on your personal life, the sort of entertaining aspects of recent days don't appeal to the same extent. The result may seem to be a seesaw quality to your nature. It's can't be helped, that's the way the planets are for you right now.

31 MONDAY
Moon Age Day 24   Moon Sign Libra

The chances are that your enthusiasm is at a peak and this is certainly no bad way to end a year. All you are really interested in today is having fun, together with making it possible for those around you to have a good time too. New Year resolutions may be put on hold, because the enjoyment is hardly likely to stop at midnight.

How to Calculate Your Rising Sign

Most astrologers agree that, next to the Sun Sign, the most important influence on any person is the Rising Sign at the time of their birth. The Rising Sign represents the astrological sign that was rising over the eastern horizon when each and every one of us came into the world. It is sometimes also called the Ascendant.

Let us suppose, for example, that you were born with the Sun in the zodiac sign of Libra. This would bestow certain characteristics on you that are likely to be shared by all other Librans. However, a Libran with Aries Rising would show a very different attitude towards life, and of course relationships, than a Libran with Pisces Rising.

For these reasons, this book shows how your zodiac Rising Sign has a bearing on all the possible positions of the Sun at birth. Simply look through the Aries table opposite.

As long as you know your approximate time of birth the graph will show you how to discover your Rising Sign.

Look across the top of the graph of your zodiac sign to find your date of birth, and down the side for your birth time (I have used Greenwich Mean Time). Where they cross is your Rising Sign. Don't forget to subtract an hour (or two) if appropriate for Summer Time.

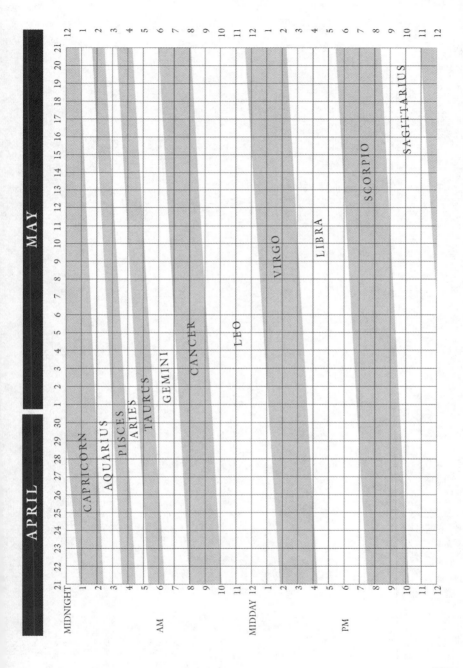

THE ZODIAC, PLANETS AND CORRESPONDENCES

The Earth revolves around the Sun once every calendar year, so when viewed from Earth the Sun appears in a different part of the sky as the year progresses. In astrology, these parts of the sky are divided into the signs of the zodiac and this means that the signs are organised in a circle. The circle begins with Aries and ends with Pisces.

Taking the zodiac sign as a starting point, astrologers then work with all the positions of planets, stars and many other factors to calculate horoscopes and birth charts and tell us what the stars have in store for us.

The table below shows the planets and Elements for each of the signs of the zodiac. Each sign belongs to one of the four Elements: Fire, Air, Earth or Water. Fire signs are creative and enthusiastic; Air signs are mentally active and thoughtful; Earth signs are constructive and practical; Water signs are emotional and have strong feelings.

It also shows the metals and gemstones associated with, or corresponding with, each sign. The correspondence is made when a metal or stone possesses properties that are held in common with a particular sign of the zodiac.

Finally, the table shows the opposite of each star sign – this is the opposite sign in the astrological circle.

Placed	Sign	Symbol	Element	Planet	Metal	Stone	Opposite
1	Aries	Ram	Fire	Mars	Iron	Bloodstone	Libra
2	Taurus	Bull	Earth	Venus	Copper	Sapphire	Scorpio
3	Gemini	Twins	Air	Mercury	Mercury	Tiger's Eye	Sagittarius
4	Cancer	Crab	Water	Moon	Silver	Pearl	Capricorn
5	Leo	Lion	Fire	Sun	Gold	Ruby	Aquarius
6	Virgo	Maiden	Earth	Mercury	Mercury	Sardonyx	Pisces
7	Libra	Scales	Air	Venus	Copper	Sapphire	Aries
8	Scorpio	Scorpion	Water	Pluto	Plutonium	Jasper	Taurus
9	Sagittarius	Archer	Fire	Jupiter	Tin	Topaz	Gemini
10	Capricorn	Goat	Earth	Saturn	Lead	Black Onyx	Cancer
11	Aquarius	Waterbearer	Air	Uranus	Uranium	Amethyst	Leo
12	Pisces	Fishes	Water	Neptune	Tin	Moonstone	Virgo